Glencoe

WORLD HISTORY

Unit 5 Resources

Glencoe
McGraw-Hill

New York, New York   Columbus, Ohio   Chicago, Illinois   Peoria, Illinois   Woodland Hills, California

Book Organization

Glencoe offers resources that accompany *Glencoe World History* to expand, enrich, review, and assess every lesson you teach and for every student you teach.

HOW THIS BOOK IS ORGANIZED

Each Unit Resources book offers blackline masters at unit, chapter, and section levels. Each book is divided into three parts—unit-based resources, chapter-based resources, and section-based resources. Tabs facilitate navigation.

UNIT-BASED RESOURCES

We have organized this book so that all unit resources appear at the beginning. Although you may choose to use the specific activities at any time during the course of unit study, Glencoe has placed these resources up front so that you can review your options. For example, the Economics and History Activities and World Literature Readings appear in the front of this book, but you may plan to use these resources in class at any time during the study of the unit.

CHAPTER-BASED AND SECTION-BASED RESOURCES

Chapter-based resources follow the unit materials. For example, Chapter 23 blackline masters appear in this book immediately following Unit 5 materials. The materials appear in the order you teach—Chapter 23 activities; Chapter 23 section activities; Chapter 24 activities; Chapter 24 section activities; and so on.

A COMPLETE ANSWER KEY

A complete answer key appears at the back of this book. This answer key includes answers for all activities in this book in the order in which the activities appear.

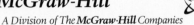

Glencoe/McGraw-Hill

A Division of The McGraw-Hill Companies

Send all inquiries to:
Glencoe/McGraw-Hill
8787 Orion Place
Columbus, Ohio 43240-4027

ISBN 0-07-829437-1

Printed in the United States of America

2 3 4 5 6 7 8 9 10   009   08 07 06 05 04 03

Table of Contents

To the Teacher

Glencoe's Unit Resources books offer varied activities to enhance the learning experience of your students.

Charting and Graphing Activities
Students organize information in either a chart or graph. These activities are designed to help students learn visually and to stimulate critical thinking abilities.

Economics and History Activities
These readings give students a greater understanding of the impact of economics on history and familiarize students with economic terms and principles. Each reading is followed by comprehension and critical thinking questions and activities.

World Literature Readings
Students read literature from some of the time periods and cultures covered by the textbook. Each selection is preceded by background information and a guided reading suggestion and is followed by comprehension and critical thinking questions.

Vocabulary Activities
These review-and-reinforcement activities help students master unfamiliar terms used in the textbook. The worksheets emphasize identification of word meanings and provide visual and kinesthetic reinforcement of language skills.

Skills Reinforcement Activities
These activities are designed to introduce and reinforce important social studies, critical thinking, technology, study, and writing skills.

Critical Thinking Skills Activities
These activities show students how to use information to make judgments, develop their own ideas, and apply what they have learned to new situations.

History and Geography Activities
Students analyze and interpret maps in relation to historical events. Students use geography skills as an aid to understanding history.

Mapping History Activities
Each activity helps students develop and practice map-based skills by analyzing and interpreting a map. The content and exercises are related to the textbook.

Historical Significance Activities
These activities relate some aspect of a time period from the textbook to something in the present day. Students see how codes of law, institutions, customs, and concerns from the past are with us today.

Cooperative Learning Activities
These extension activities offer students clear directions for working together on a variety of activities that enrich prior learning.

History Simulation Activities
Students work in small groups to explore a theme, topic, or concept from the textbook. Many of these activities use a game or simulation format to stimulate student interest. Groups document their efforts by completing a chart, diagram, or planning sheet.

Time Line Activities
These activities are designed to reinforce the dates of major events in world history and to help students learn the chronological order of those events. Each activity includes a time line labeled with events and dates. Students answer questions based on the time line.

Linking Past and Present Activities
Students analyze readings that describe past and present ideas, customs, art, architecture, scientific breakthroughs, and governments. Students learn that individuals, societies, and cultures continue to grapple with many of the same issues.

People in World History Profiles
These biographical sketches of significant figures from world history expose students to a diversity of cultures and time periods. Questions emphasize the role of individuals in historical events.

Primary Source Readings
Students study the original written works of people throughout history. Each selection is preceded by an introduction and a guided reading suggestion and is followed by questions that allow students to analyze and interpret the material.

Reteaching Activities
These varied activities enable students to visualize the connections among facts in their textbook. Graphs, charts, tables, and concept maps are among the many types of graphic organizers used.

Enrichment Activities
These activities introduce content that is different from, but related to, the themes, ideas, and information in the textbook. Students develop a broader and deeper understanding of the relationship of historical events to the contemporary world.

World Art and Music Activities
Students are exposed to art and music from around the world. Critical thinking questions help students to understand art and music within a historical context.

Guided Reading Activities
These activities provide help for students who are having difficulty comprehending the text. Students fill in information in the guided reading outlines, sentence completion activities, or other information-organizing exercises as they read the textbook.

Glencoe

WORLD HISTORY

Unit 5 Resources
The Twentieth-Century Crisis: 1914–1945

UNIT 5

World Literature Reading 5

"The Kabuliwallah" is set in India around 1890. The family in the story is Hindu, and the members belong to the Brahman caste. The Indian castes did not socialize or intermarry, but the caste system would not have applied to a Kabuliwallah, a Muslim from Kabul, Afghanistan.

About the Author **Rabindranath Tagore** (1861–1941) is one of India's most famous writers, winner of the Nobel Prize for Literature in 1913. Born into a wealthy and famous family, Tagore was educated in England and returned to India to manage his father's estate. He was a pacifist and deeply moved by the plight of the poor, themes that run through his stories. Tagore also wrote poems, plays, and essays. In addition, he was a skilled musician, painter, and actor.

GUIDED READING As you read "The Kabuliwallah," think about the messages about compassion that are conveyed in this story.

The Kabuliwallah

My five-year-old daughter Mini cannot live without chattering. I really believe that in all her life she has not wasted a minute in silence. Her mother is often vexed at this, and would stop her prattle, but I would not. To see Mini quiet is unnatural, and I cannot bear it long. And so my own talk with her is always lively.

One morning, for instance, when I was in the midst of the seventeenth chapter of my new novel, my little Mini stole into the room, and putting her hand into mine, said: "Father! Ramdayal the door-keeper calls a crow a crew! He doesn't know anything, does he?"

Before I could explain to her the differences of language in this world, she was embarked on the full tide of another subject. "What do you think, Father? Bhola says there

is an elephant in the clouds, blowing water out of his trunk, and that is why it rains!"

And then, darting off anew, while I sat still making ready some reply to this last saying, "Father! what relation is Mother to you?"

"My dear little sister in the law!" I murmured involuntarily to myself, but with a grave face contrived to answer: "Go and play with Bhola, Mini! I am busy!"

The window of my room overlooks the road. The child had seated herself at my feet near my table, and was playing softly, drumming on her knees. I was hard at work on my seventeenth chapter, where Pratap Singh, the hero, had just caught Kanchanlata, the heroine, in his arms, and was about to escape with her by the third story window of the castle, when all of a

World Literature Reading 5

From "The Kabuliwallah" (continued)

sudden Mini left her play, and ran to the window, crying, "A Kabuliwallah! a Kabuliwallah!" Sure enough in the street below was a Kabuliwallah, passing slowly along. He wore the loose soiled clothing of his people, with a tall turban; there was a bag on his back, and he carried boxes of grapes in his hand.

I cannot tell what were my daughter's feelings at the sight of this man, but she began to call him loudly. "Ah!" I thought, "he will come in, and my seventeenth chapter will never be finished!" At which exact moment the Kabuliwallah turned, and looked up at the child. When she saw this, overcome by terror, she fled to her mother's protection, and disappeared. She had a blind belief that inside the bag, which the big man carried, there were perhaps two or three other children like herself. The peddler meanwhile entered my doorway, and greeted me with a smiling face.

So precarious was the position of my hero and my heroine that my first impulse was to stop and buy something, since the man had been called. I made some small purchases, and a conversation began about Abdur Rahman, the Russians, the English, and the Frontier Policy.[1]

As he was about to leave, he asked: "And where is the little girl, sir?"

And I, thinking that Mini must get rid of her false fear, had her brought out.

She stood by my chair, and looked at the Kabuliwallah and his bag. He offered her nuts and raisins, but she would not be tempted, and only clung the closer to me, with all her doubts increased.

This was their first meeting.

One morning, however, not many days later, as I was leaving the house, I was startled to find Mini, seated on a bench near the door, laughing and talking, with the great Kabuliwallah at her feet. In all her life, it appeared, my small daughter had never found so patient a listener, save her father. And already the corner of her little sari was stuffed with almonds and raisins, the gift of her visitor. "Why did you give her those?" I said, and taking out an eight-anna bit,[2] I handed it to him. The man accepted the money without demur, and slipped it into his pocket.

Alas, on my return an hour later, I found the unfortunate coin had made twice its own worth of trouble! For the Kabuliwallah had given it to Mini, and her mother, catching sight of the bright round object, had pounced on the child with: "Where did you get that eight-anna bit?"

"The Kabuliwallah gave it to me," said Mini cheerfully.

"The Kabuliwallah gave it to you!" cried her mother, much shocked. "Oh, Mini! how could you take it from him?"

I, entering at the moment, saved her from impending disaster, and proceeded to make my own inquiries.

It was not the first or second time, I found, that the two had met. The Kabuliwallah had overcome the child's first terror by a judicious bribery of nuts and almonds, and the two were now great friends.

They had many quaint jokes, which afforded them much amusement. Seated in front of him, looking down on his gigantic frame in all her tiny dignity, Mini would ripple her face with laughter, and begin: "O Kabuliwallah, Kabuliwallah, what have you got in your bag?"

And he would reply, in the nasal accents of the mountaineer: "An elephant!" Not much cause for merriment, perhaps; but

---

1 **Frontier Policy:** Both the Russians and the British wanted to extend their frontiers into Afghanistan. The Afghani Abdur Rahman, leader of Afghanistan from 1880 to 1901, opposed this.

2 **eight-anna bit:** an Indian coin worth about eight cents at that time

World Literature Reading 5

From "The Kabuliwallah" (continued)

how they both enjoyed the witticism! And for me, this child's talk with a grown-up man had always in it something strangely fascinating.

Then the Kabuliwallah, not to be behindhand, would take his turn: "Well, little one, and when are you going to the father-in-law's house?"

Now most small Bengali maidens have heard long ago about the father-in-law's house; but we, being a little new-fangled, had kept these things from our child, and Mini at this question must have been a trifle bewildered. But she would not show it, and with ready tact replied: "Are *you* going there?"

Amongst men of the Kabuliwallah's class, however, it is well known that the words *father-in-law's house* have a double meaning. It is a euphemism for jail, the place where we are well cared for, at no expense to ourselves. In this sense would the sturdy peddler take my daughter's question. "Ah," he would say, shaking his fist at an invisible policeman, "I will thrash my father-in-law!" Hearing this, and picturing the poor discomfited relative, Mini would go off into peals of laughter, in which her formidable friend would join.

These were autumn mornings, the very time of year when kings of old went forth to conquest; and I, never stirring from my little corner in Calcutta, would let my mind wander over the whole world. At the very name of another country, my heart would go out to it, and at the sight of a foreigner in the streets, I would fall to weaving a network of dreams—the mountains, the glens, and the forests of his distant home, with his cottage in its setting, and the free and independent life of far-away wilds. Perhaps the scenes of travel conjure themselves up before me, and repass in my imagination all the more vividly, because I lead such a

vegetable existence that a call to travel would fall upon me like a thunderbolt. In the presence of the Kabuliwallah, I was immediately transported to the foot of arid mountain peaks, with narrow little defiles twisting in and out amongst their towering heights. I could see the string of camels bearing the merchandise, and the company of turbaned merchants carrying some of their queer old firearms, and some of their spears, journeying downward towards the plains. I could see—but at some such point Mini's mother would intervene, imploring me to "beware of that man."

Mini's mother is unfortunately a very timid lady. Whenever she hears a noise in the street, or sees people coming towards the house, she always jumps to the conclusion that they are either thieves, or drunkards, or snakes, or tigers, or malaria, or cockroaches, or caterpillars, or an English sailor. Even after all these years of experience, she is not able to overcome her terror. So she was full of doubts about the Kabuliwallah, and used to beg me to keep a watchful eye on him.

I tried to laugh her fear gently away, but then she would turn round on me seriously, and ask me solemn questions.

Were children never kidnapped?

Was it, then, not true that there was slavery in Kabul?

Was it so very absurd that this big man should be able to carry off a tiny child?

I urged that, though not impossible, it was highly improbable. But this was not enough, and her dread persisted. As it was indefinite, however, it did not seem right to forbid the man the house, and the intimacy went on unchecked.

Once a year in the middle of January Rahmun, the Kabuliwallah, was in the habit of returning to his country, and as the time approached he would be very busy, going

13

World Literature Reading 5

From "The Kabuliwallah" (continued)

from house to house collecting his debts. This year, however, he could always find time to come and see Mini. It would have seemed to an outsider that there was some conspiracy between the two, for when he could not come in the morning, he would appear in the evening.

Even to me it was a little startling now and then, in the corner of a dark room, suddenly to surprise this tall, loose-garmented, much bebagged man; but when Mini would run in smiling, with her, "O! Kabuliwallah! Kabuliwallah!" and the two friends, so far apart in age, would subside into their old laughter and their old jokes, I felt reassured.

One morning, a few days before he had made up his mind to go, I was correcting my proof sheets in my study. It was chilly weather. Through the window the rays of the sun touched my feet, and the slight warmth was very welcome. It was almost eight o'clock, and the early pedestrians were returning home, with their heads covered. All at once, I heard an uproar in the street, and, looking out, saw Rahmun being led away bound between two policeman, and behind them a crowd of curious boys. There were blood-stains on the clothes of the Kabuliwallah, and one of the policemen carried a knife. Hurrying out, I stopped them, and inquired what it all meant. Partly from one, partly from another, I gathered that a certain neighbor had owed the peddler something for a Rampuri shawl, but had falsely denied having bought it, and that in the course of the quarrel, Rahmun had struck him. Now in the heat of this excitement, the prisoner began calling his enemy all sorts of names, when suddenly in a veranda of my house appeared my little Mini, with her usual exclamation: "O! Kabuliwallah! Kabuliwallah!" Rahmun's face

lighted up as he turned to her. He had no bag under his arm today, so she could not discuss the elephant with him. She at once therefore proceeded to the next question, "Are you going to the father-in-law's house?" Rahmun laughed and said: "Just where I am going, little one!" Then seeing that the reply did not amuse the child, he held up his fettered hands. "Ah," he said, "I would have thrashed that old father-in-law, but my hands are bound!"

On a charge of murderous assault, Rahmun was sentenced to some years' imprisonment.

Time passed away, and he was not remembered. The accustomed work in the accustomed place was ours, and the thought of the once-free mountaineer spending his years in prison seldom or never occurred to us. Even my lighthearted Mini, I am ashamed to say, forgot her old friend. New companions filled her life. As she grew older, she spent more of her time with girls. So much time indeed did she spend with them that she came no more, as she used to do, to her father's room. I was scarcely on speaking terms with her.

Years had passed away. It was once more autumn and we had made arrangements for our Mini's marriage. It was to take place during the Puja Holidays.[3] With Durga returning to Kailas, the light of our home was also to depart to her husband's house, and leave her father's in the shadow.

The morning was bright. After the rains, there was a sense of ablution in the air, and the sun-rays looked like pure gold. So bright were they that they gave a beautiful radiance even to the sordid brick walls of our Calcutta lanes. Since early dawn today the wedding-pipes had been sounding, and at each beat my own heart throbbed. The wail of the tune, "Bhairavi," seemed to

---

3 Puja Holidays are an autumn festival celebrating Durga, the Hindu mother goddess. Durga returns to her husband at the top of Mount Kailas.

World Literature Reading 5

From "The Kabuliwallah" (continued)

intensify my pain at the approaching separation. My Mini was to be married tonight.

From early morning noise and bustle had pervaded the house. In the courtyard the canopy had to be slung on its bamboo poles; the chandeliers with their tinkling sound must be hung in each room and veranda. There was no end of hurry and excitement. I was sitting in my study, looking through the accounts, when someone entered, saluting respectfully, and stood before me. It was Rahmun the Kabuliwallah. At first I did not recognize him. He had no bag, nor the long hair, nor the same vigor that he used to have. But he smiled, and I knew him again.

"When did you come, Rahmun?" I asked him.

"Last evening," he said, "I was released from jail."

The words struck harsh upon my ears. I had never before talked with one who had wounded his fellow, and my heart shrank within itself, when I realized this, for I felt that the day would have been better-omened had he not turned up.

"There are ceremonies going on," I said, "and I am busy. Could you perhaps come another day?"

At once he turned to go; but as he reached the door he hesitated and said: "May I not see the little one, sir, for a moment?" It was his belief that Mini was still the same. He had pictured her running to him as she used, calling, "O Kabuliwallah! Kabuliwallah!" He had imagined too that they would laugh and talk together, just as of old. In fact, in memory of former days he had brought, carefully wrapped up in paper, a few almonds and raisins and grapes, obtained somehow from a countryman, for his own little fund was dispersed.

I said once again: "There is a ceremony in the house, and you will not be able to see anyone today."

The man's face fell. He looked wistfully at me for a moment, said "Good morning," and went out.

I felt a little sorry, and would have called him back, but I found he was returning of his own accord. He came close up to me, holding out his offerings, and said: "I brought these few things, sir, for the little one. Will you give them to her?"

I took them and was going to pay him, but he caught my hand and said: "You are very kind, sir! Keep me in your recollection. Do not offer me money!—You have a little girl; I too have one like her in my own home. I think of her, and bring fruits to your child, not to make a profit for myself."

Saying this, he put his hand inside his big loose robe, and brought out a small and dirty piece of paper. With great care he unfolded this, and smoothed it out with both hands on my table. It bore the impression of a little hand. Not a photograph. Not a drawing. The impression of an ink-smeared hand laid flat on the paper. This touch of his own little daughter had been always on his heart, as he had come year after year to Calcutta, to sell his wares in the streets.

Tears came to my eyes. I forgot that he was a poor Kabuli fruit-seller, while I was—but no, what was I more than he? He also was a father.

That impression of the hand of his little Parvati in her distant mountain home reminded me of my own little Mini.

I sent for Mini immediately from the inner apartment. Many difficulties were raised, but I would not listen. Clad in the red silk of her wedding day, with the sandal paste on her forehead, and adorned as a young bride, Mini came, and stood bashfully before me.

The Kabuliwallah looked a little staggered at the apparition. He could not revive their old friendship. At last he smiled and

World Literature Reading 5

From "The Kabuliwallah" (continued)

said: "Little one, are you going to your father-in-law's house?"

But Mini now understood the meaning of the word "father-in-law," and she could not reply to him as of old. She flushed up at the question, and stood before him with her bride-like face turned down.

I remembered the day when the Kabuliwallah and my Mini had first met, and I felt sad. When she had gone, Rahmun heaved a deep sigh and sat down on the floor. The idea had suddenly come to him that his daughter too must have grown in this long time, and that he would have to make friends with her anew. Assuredly he would not find her as he used to know her. And besides, what might not have happened to her in these eight years?

The marriage-pipes sounded, and the mild autumn sun streamed round us. But Rahmun sat in the little Calcutta lane, and saw before him the barren mountains of Afghanistan.

I took out a bank-note and gave it to him, saying: "Go back to your own daughter, Rahmun, in your own country, and may the happiness of your meeting bring good fortune to my child!"

Having made this present, I had to curtail some of the festivities. I could not have the electric lights I had intended, nor the military band, and the ladies of the house were despondent at it. But to me the wedding feast was all the brighter for the thought that in a distant land a long-lost father met again with his only child.

DIRECTIONS: Answer the following questions in the space provided.

Interpreting the Reading

1. What are the two meanings of "going to your father-in-law's house"?

   _____

   _____

2. The Kabuliwallah has a name, yet the narrator refers to him throughout most of the story only as the "Kabuliwallah." Why?

   _____

3. Why does the narrator cry when he sees the handprint from the Kabuliwallah's daughter?

   _____

   _____

Critical Thinking

4. **Recognizing Ideologies** What does Tagore suggest about the responsibilities that fathers have in raising their children?

   _____

   _____

   _____

16

Skills Reinforcement Activity 23

Interpreting Military Movements on Maps

When looking at a map that explains military information such as battles, troop movements, and conquered territory, it is important to read the map key. The key tells you what various colors and symbols on the map represent.

DIRECTIONS: Study the key to the map below, then use the map to answer the questions in the spaces provided.

1. a. Before the war began, to what country did Warsaw belong?

_____

b. Was Finland part of Russia after World War I?

_____

c. Judging from the map, which was bigger, the Russian Empire or the Soviet Union?

_____

2. a. The White Russian armies attacked from which two main directions?

_____

_____

b. Who commanded these armies?

_____

3. Which two of the following were not controlled by the Communists at the end of 1917: Moscow, Petrograd, Kharkov, Kiev, Minsk?

_____

Western Russia at the time of Bolshevik control

──	Boundary of Russian Empire, 1914
- - -	Eastern Front, Mar. 1917
★	Towns under Bolshevik control Nov–Dec. 1917
○	Towns not under Bolshevik control
└	Russian territory occupied by Central Powers 1918
	Area controlled by Bolsheviks, Oct. 1919
	Soviet borders, Mar. 1921
	White Russian army
←	Non-Russian anti-Bolshevik forces

4. Which troops invaded from the city of Murmansk? _____

5. The French fleet attacked which cities in the south?

_____

6. Which anti-Bolshevik army attacked the city of Minsk? _____

7. Which groups made up the Entente fleet arriving at Archangel?

_____

Critical Thinking Skills Activity 23 | Determining Cause and Effect

When historians attempt to record and make sense of the events of a particular era, they look at causes and results of those events. Often they discover a series of events that are related by cause and effect: One event causes the next, which causes the next, and so on. This kind of series is called a chain of events.

DIRECTIONS: Read the following passage about World War I. Then fill in the diagram to illustrate the cause-and-effect relationships between the events described.

Fearing an attack by Germany, which had signed an alliance with Austria-Hungary, France sought its own security arrangement with Russia. This agreement required the parties to support each other against German or Austro-Hungarian aggression. Counting on French support, Russia mobilized against Germany and Austria-Hungary in defense of the Slavs in Serbia. Germany then gave France an ultimatum to remain neutral, but when its conditions were not met, it declared war on France.

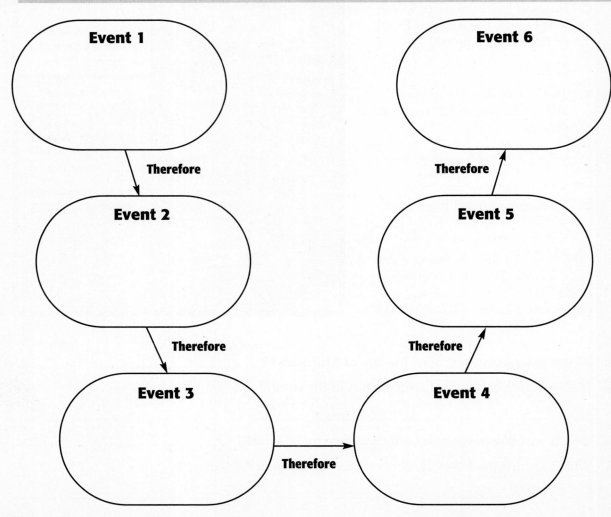

Event 1

Therefore

Event 2

Therefore

Event 3

Therefore

Event 4

Therefore

Event 5

Therefore

Event 6

★ HISTORY AND GEOGRAPHY ACTIVITY 23

The Battle of the Somme

Where there had once been green forests and groves, there was now only the occasional leafless, branchless tree. Autumn had come to the Somme valley of France in 1916. But it was an artificial autumn, brought on by bombs, bullets, and hand grenades. How did advances in military technology change the nature of warfare with the outbreak of World War I?

Before World War I, vacationing Parisians used to flock north to the Somme River. The waterway flowed lazily through a gentle countryside dotted with rich farms, quaint villages, and thickly wooded hills. Happy to escape the stresses of city life, the Parisians swam in the Somme, strolled through the woods, and nibbled on bread and cheese from the local bakeries and farms.

The tourists barely dented the local food supply. For hundreds of years, the rolling plains around the Somme had been one of France's leading agricultural regions. Wheat, barley, oats, sugar beets, and all manner of fruits and vegetables grew in the area's fertile

soil. Farmers raised cattle by the thousands and produced cheese and butter by the ton.

When the opposing armies arrived at the Somme in 1916, they dug trenches

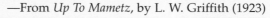

A Desolate Landscape

I reached a [crossroads] where four lanes broadened into a confused patch of destruction. Fallen trees, shell holes, a hurriedly dug trench beginning and ending in an uncertain manner, abandoned rifles, broken branches with their sagging leaves, an unopened box of ammunition, sandbags half-filled with bombs, a derelict machine-gun propping up the head of an immobile figure in uniform, with a belt of ammunition drooping from the breech into a pile of red-stained earth—this is the livery of War. Shells were falling, over and short, near and wide, to show that somewhere over the hill a gunner was playing the part of blind fate for all who walked past this well-marked spot. Here, in the struggle between bursting iron and growing timber, iron had triumphed. . . .

—From *Up To Mametz,* by L. W. Griffith (1923)

"Over the top!" resounded along Allied lines as soldiers poured from their trenches into No Man's Land. The scarred remains of a forest show the devastating effects of trench warfare on the countryside near the Somme River.

HISTORY AND GEOGRAPHY ACTIVITY 23 (continued)

instead of seed rows. Their constant artillery fire soon destroyed the land between the trenches, turning it into a desolate landscape known as No Man's Land. It was No Tree's Land as well, because nothing could stand up to the powerful artillery shells.

Different groups of people interact with their environment in different ways. The farmers of the Somme, for example, grew wheat, oats, and vegetables in the fertile soil of the plains, but they grew few crops on the surrounding hills. It was difficult for them to clear the trees from the hills and plant crops on the hillsides. Besides, the soil was richer on the plains.

The soldiers had a different opinion of the Somme's geographic features. They prized the hills and dreaded the plains. The hills gave commanding views across a wide area and were easy to defend. The plains, on the other hand, offered little protection and exposed soldiers to attack from all sides.

APPLYING GEOGRAPHY TO HISTORY

DIRECTIONS: Answer the questions below in the space provided.

1. Why did soldiers and farmers have different opinions of the Somme's geographic features? Which features were important to each group? Why?

   _____

   _____

2. Compare the impacts of farming and warfare on the Somme.

   _____

3. What impact do you think a modern war would have on the Somme? Why?

   _____

Critical Thinking

4. **Evaluating Information** Which aspects of the Somme's geography might interest a modern factory owner? Why?

   _____

   _____

Activity

5. Do you think the land of the Somme ever returned to its prewar condition? Working with a group, research the Somme or another famous World War I battlefield. Try to answer the following questions: How did war transform the land? Which parts of the land were able to recover? How long did the recovery take? Which parts were unable to recover? Why? Report your findings to the class.

Mapping History Activity 23

World War I in the Balkans

When fighting broke out in Europe in 1914, the Allies and the Central Powers fought for control of the Balkan Peninsula and the Ottoman Empire.

DIRECTIONS: Use the map to answer the questions and complete the activity that follow. Use a separate sheet of paper.

1. Which countries in the Balkan Peninsula sided with the Allies?

2. Why was it important for the Allies to attempt the Gallipoli invasion?

3. Why did it make sense for both Austria-Hungary and Bulgaria to attack Romania?

4. Read the following passage, then follow the instructions below.

The Central Powers led an offensive against Serbia in 1915. Attacks were launched from Austria-Hungary just north of Belgrade and from Sofia. The armies came together west of Skopje near the Albanian border. Another attack came from Sarajevo and pushed south into Albania. In 1916 the German

Balkan Peninsula and Surrounding Regions, 1914

forces that had succeeded in moving the Eastern Front into Russia turned south to conquer Romania. Falkenhayn led an offensive from several points in southeastern Austria-Hungary toward the capital city of Bucharest and the Black Sea port of Constanz. Mackensen led forces from northeastern Bulgaria to these same cities. All of the territory north of the line running from Valona to Salonika fell into Central Powers' hands.

The Allies finally were able to counterattack. In 1918 they moved in from Greek territory. The French and British troops arrived at the port of Salonika. From there, they drove north through Serbia to Belgrade and from there to Budapest. The Central Powers were unable to halt the advances of the Allied troops. Other regiments battled on to Sofia and to Constantinople in order to end the Central Powers' dominance over the peninsula.

a. Using a red marker, draw arrows to show the movements of the Central Powers' troops.

b. Shade in the territory conquered by the Central Powers.

c. Using a blue marker, draw in the counteroffensive staged by the Allies in 1918 to win back the Balkan Peninsula.

Historical Significance Activity 23

The Plight of Refugees

Among the global catastrophes that threatened peace during the 1990s was the flow of refugees from areas of conflict toward safety. This type of problem is not new. In 1945 millions of German Holocaust survivors were displaced after the collapse of Hitler's Third Reich. In 1979 hundreds of thousands of Vietnamese fled their war-torn country in makeshift boats, hoping to find a haven in foreign lands. More recently, wars in Afghanistan and the Balkans have created enormous refugee populations. Read the following passage from a March 1996 newspaper editorial about refugees from the Bosnian civil war.

As many as 2 million Bosnians lost their homes in the civil war there and are now scattered and adrift across Europe. Many in that refugee diaspora [dispersion] will soon attempt to put down new roots in their old land. The international powers, which have invested so much in fostering military and political stability in the former Yugoslavia, owe it to the Bosnians and to the cause of peace to help in the resettlement. For if the refugee effort fails on a broad scale or is mired in widespread turmoil, all of the international community's other efforts will be hardpressed to succeed. . . .

But the number of returnees to date pales beside the 830,000 more dislocated persons UNHCR [United Nations High Commissioner for Refugees] anticipates will try to resettle in Bosnia by year-end, beginning in the spring. The first step in staving off a potential fiasco is filling the $353 million Balkan funding request the UNHCR issued to donor nations earlier this month. Washington legislators must not allow campaign politicking to prevent the United States from contributing its share.

The second step is encouraging other international development agencies to follow the lead of the World Bank, which last week announced a $450 million loan package for Bosnian redevelopment. Especially important to the reconstruction agenda will be support for de-mining. About 3 million land mines have been sown in Bosnia, many in residential areas, and the painstaking, unglamorous job of removal will in many cases determine the success of the resettlement efforts.

DIRECTIONS: Complete the activities described below. Write your editorial on a separate sheet of paper.

1. Discuss the passage with a small group of classmates. What is the writer's point of view? Do you agree or disagree?

2. Working individually, write an editorial supporting or rebutting the argument made in the passage.

3. Meet again with your group to share and discuss completed editorials.

Time Line Activity 23

War and Revolution

DIRECTIONS: Look at the events listed on the time line. Write each event in the chart below next to the theme it represents, caused, or resulted from. In the right-hand column, explain how each event is related to the theme. Try to place events in more than one category. Examples have been started for you.

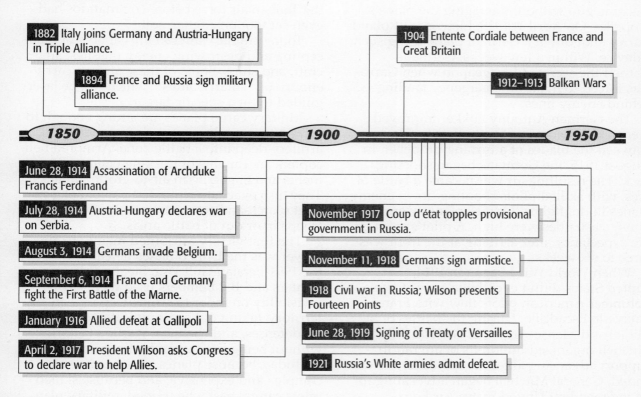

1882 Italy joins Germany and Austria-Hungary in Triple Alliance.

1894 France and Russia sign military alliance.

1904 Entente Cordiale between France and Great Britain

1912–1913 Balkan Wars

1850   1900   1950

June 28, 1914 Assassination of Archduke Francis Ferdinand

July 28, 1914 Austria-Hungary declares war on Serbia.

August 3, 1914 Germans invade Belgium.

September 6, 1914 France and Germany fight the First Battle of the Marne.

January 1916 Allied defeat at Gallipoli

April 2, 1917 President Wilson asks Congress to declare war to help Allies.

November 1917 Coup d'état topples provisional government in Russia.

November 11, 1918 Germans sign armistice.

1918 Civil war in Russia; Wilson presents Fourteen Points

June 28, 1919 Signing of Treaty of Versailles

1921 Russia's White armies admit defeat.

Events Relating to Themes

Theme	Event	Explanation
Cooperation	Italy joins Germany and Austria-Hungary in Triple Alliance.	Alliance brings countries together to support one another against aggressors.
Conflict		
Revolution		
Internationalism		

Linking Past and Present Activity 23

Air Warfare

THEN "Aviation is good sport," proclaimed French General Foch in 1914, "but for warfare it is useless!" One reason for the general's opinion was that early aircraft carried no weapons. However, less than one year later, the French had figured out how to fire a machine gun without damaging the plane's propeller. On April 1, 1915, Lieutenant Roland Garros shot down a German plane using such a device. Within a few weeks, Germans learned the secret of his weapon when Garros was forced to make an emergency landing behind enemy lines.

The German Anthony Fokker improved French technology, timing bullets to fire between the blades of a turning propeller. In August 1915, the Germans began shooting back. The resulting air war became a battle of aces, with skilled pilots shooting down enemy planes in dogfights. Because planes were flimsy, casualties were high. A pilot's average life expectancy after arriving at the front was three to six weeks.

When World War I began in 1914, the United States didn't even have an air force. Volunteer American pilots flew with France's Lafayette Escadrille. During the battles of St. Mihiel and Mense-Argonne, General Billy Mitchell organized hundreds of aircraft to support advancing allied troops. After the war ended, General Mitchell began advocating for an independent United States Air Force. Mitchell was one of the few military personnel who realized that planes could support ground attacks and even sink ships.

NOW Today, some wars are fought almost entirely from the air. In 1999, NATO forces used bombers rather than ground troops to end Serbian genocide of ethnic Albanians. When the United States and its allies pursued Osama bin Laden in 2001, air strikes destroyed the Taliban air force before commandos had even set foot on Afghan soil.

Today, military aircraft are capable of intercepting and destroying enemy missiles, aircraft, and ships. Some of these aircraft carry enormous "smart bombs," which can be laser-guided to hit a specific target.

Military cargo planes are strong enough to carry heavy equipment such as tanks or artillery deep into a battle zone. Armored helicopters are capable of tracking enemy movements and engaging in air-to-ground attacks. They also evacuate wounded personnel, conduct search-and-rescue missions, and move troops in or out of battle areas.

The first victory attributed mainly to air power was the United States defeat of Iraq in the 1991 Persian Gulf War. Stealth F-117A fighters and B-2 bombers used their virtual invisibility on radar to strike deep into enemy territory, taking out communications centers, air defenses, and chemical warfare factories without being fired upon by Iraqi forces.

Today, because planes have become so complex and expensive, and because skilled pilots cannot easily be trained, military planners are experimenting with unmanned aircraft or drones for combat purposes. For example, the X-plane *Pegasus*, an unmanned plane capable of identifying and destroying enemy targets, fires a pain cannon that is capable of disabling an enemy without causing lasting harm.

CRITICAL THINKING

Directions: Answer the following questions on a separate sheet of paper.

1. **Making comparisons:** Contrast the importance of combat aircraft today with its importance in World War I.
2. **Drawing conclusions:** Reflect on the statement "The country that controls the air will always win the war." Do you agree or disagree with this statement? Explain.

3. **Synthesizing information:** Do research in the library or on the Internet to learn more about the history of air warfare. Choose one person or event that you think is significant to air warfare. Write a brief explanation of why that person or event should be included in a new video about air warfare.

People in World History Activity **23**

Profile 1

Archduke Francis Ferdinand (1863–1914)

Describing the death of a soldier in Shakespeare's *Macbeth*, the king's son says, "Nothing in his life became him like the leaving it." Archduke Francis Ferdinand, too, is remembered for the way he died, for his death was the spark that ignited World War I.

Francis Ferdinand was born in Graz, Austria, the eldest son of Archduke Charles Louis and the nephew of Emperor Francis Joseph. When he was 12 years old, Francis Ferdinand inherited the title Archduke of Austria-Este. He became heir to the Austro-Hungarian Empire in 1899, after the deaths of his father and his cousin, Crown Prince Rudolph. However, since Francis Ferdinand's health was poor, most people assumed that the throne would go to his younger brother Otto. This made Francis Ferdinand very bitter. There were other conflicts as well.

Francis Ferdinand was deeply in love with Countess Sophia Chotek, duchess of Hohenberg. The countess was of a much lower social rank than Francis Ferdinand. As the heir apparent to the Austro-Hungarian Empire, he was expected to marry someone of equal rank, such as the queen or princess of a great empire. After much strife, Francis Ferdinand was allowed to marry Sophia—but only after he relinquished all claim to the throne for his children. The morganatic marriage disallowing Sophia and their children any of the rights guaranteed by Francis Ferdinand's status took place in 1900.

Francis Ferdinand tried to influence foreign affairs, but he had little success because of limitations placed on his power by Francis Joseph, who remained emperor. From 1906 on, however, he did exert greater influence on military issues. In 1913, he became the inspector general of the army, but his time in this office was tragically cut short.

In June 1914, he and his wife were assassinated at Sarajevo by the Serb nationalist Gavrilo Princip. World War I began a month later, when Austria declared war against Serbia.

CHAPTER 23

REVIEWING THE PROFILE

Directions: Answer the following questions on a separate sheet of paper.

1. Why is Archduke Francis Ferdinand significant in history?

2. What made Archduke Francis Ferdinand bitter?

3. What were the expectations about the kind of person the Archduke would marry?

4. **Critical Thinking** **Determining Cause and Effect.** What were the consequences of Archduke Francis Ferdinand's marriage?

5. **Critical Thinking** **Predicting Consequences.** What influence do you think Archduke Francis Ferdinand might have had on history had he lived? Explain your answer.

People in World History Activity 23 — Profile 2

Rosa Luxemburg (1871–1919)

> Freedom only for the supporters of the government— only for the members of one party, however numerous they may be—is no freedom at all. Freedom is always and exclusively for one who thinks differently.
>
> From *The Russian Revolution* (1916) by Rosa Luxemburg

CHAPTER 23

Rosa Luxemburg was a Marxist revolutionary and one of the founders of the German Communist Party. Nicknamed "Bloody Rosa" for her fiery revolutionary spirit, she never ceased demanding political power and economic equality for workers.

Born in 1871 in the Russian section of Poland, Luxemburg was the youngest of five children in a lower-middle-class Jewish family. She was crippled, and her health was very poor. Despite her physical ailments, Luxemburg never turned away from danger or physical activity. While still a teenager, she became involved in revolutionary activities. These activities could very likely have landed her in prison. As a result, in 1889 she moved to Switzerland, as many of her fellow revolutionaries were doing. In Zurich she studied law and political theory, earning her doctorate in 1898.

That same year, she moved to Germany to work in the Social Democratic Party. To obtain German citizenship, she married Gustav Lubeck. A year later, she established her reputation as a brilliant thinker with her book *Social Reform or Revolution?*

When the Russian Revolution of 1905 broke out, Luxemburg went to Warsaw to take part in the struggle. She was arrested and jailed. That revolution was the most important experience in Luxemburg's life. Until then, she believed that the world revolution would begin in Germany. Now she believed that it would start in Russia.

After her release, she returned to Berlin and became a teacher in the Social Democratic Party school. At the same time, she set forth her political theories in greater detail. She supported mass strikes as the most important way to bring about a Socialist victory.

Luxemburg spoke out strongly against World War I and helped organize the Spartacus League, which later became the German Communist Party. Imprisoned again for her revolutionary activities, she nonetheless continued to write.

In 1919, Luxemburg was murdered by soldiers in Berlin. After her death, her reputation spread among revolutionaries, and she became a martyr for their cause.

REVIEWING THE PROFILE

Directions: Answer the following questions on a separate sheet of paper.

1. Why did Luxemburg move to Switzerland in 1889?

2. What was the most important political experience of Luxemburg's life? Why?

3. **Critical Thinking** Recognizing Ideologies. Why did Luxemburg want to overthrow the existing political structure? What strategies did she support to accomplish social change?

4. **Critical Thinking** Drawing Conclusions. Do you admire Luxemburg? Why or why not?

PRIMARY SOURCE READING 23

The Letters of Lenin

Lenin became a revolutionary after his brother was executed for plotting to kill the czar. As a student, Lenin had read Karl Marx and developed a strong belief in revolutionary socialism. This meant abolishing private property and establishing a classless society to be set up after a revolution. Lenin fled to Geneva to escape czarist secret service. From Geneva he wrote letters to accomplices advising them on how to organize the workers and how to get them to join the Russian Social Democratic Labor party. The Bolsheviks were the majority group within the party and advocated revolutionary actions. Their publication was *Vpered*, which means "forward." The Mensheviks were the minority group and were less radical than the Bolsheviks. Lenin returned to Russia in 1917. After the revolution in that year, the Bolsheviks were in power, and the Russian Social Democratic Labor party had become the Communist Party.

Guided Reading *In this selection, read to learn what problems Lenin faced in organizing workers and persuading them to attend the meeting of the Third Communist Party Congress as delegates.*

To S. I. Gusev in Petersburg, member of the Bureau of Bolshevik Committees [Geneva, the beginning of March, 1905]

My dear Friend,

Very many thanks for your letters. You are simply saving us from foreign impressions. Do continue this. For God's sake, get hold of letters from the workers themselves. Why do they not write?? It is a positive disgrace! Your detailed account of the agitation in the Committee at the election to the Shidlovsky Commission [a commission to try to solve workers' problems] was magnificent. We shall print it.

Another question: have you accepted the six selected workers for the Committee? Answer without fail. We strongly advise you to accept workers on to the Committee, at any rate half. Without this you will not strengthen yourselves against the Mensheviks, who will send strong reinforcements from here.

No one writes from the Bureau about the Congress. This makes us anxious, for the Nymph's [a nickname of one of Gusev's colleagues] optimism (and partly your own), that the Central Committee consent to the Congress is a plus, inspires us with gigantic fears. It is as clear as daylight to us that the Central Committee wanted to fool you. You must be a pessimist so far as the Central Committee is concerned. For God's sake do not trust it! Take advantage of the moment to force Menshevik Committees and especially weak Committees to appear. It is extremely important to exert pressure on Kiev, Rostov, and Kharkov. We *know* that in these three centers there are "Vpered" supporters, both among the *workers* and the intelligentsia. Whatever happens, they must send delegates to the Congress with a consultative vote. Write to the Nymph and the Demon [another member of the Bureau] about all this. The same applies to the Moscow printers. It is a great pity that the Bureau did not publish our decision to invite Workers' Organisations to the Congress: that was a *terrible* mistake. Put it right at once and without fail.

I would strongly advise an agitation among the three hundred organised [Bolshevik] workers in St. Petersburg that they should send *at their own expense* one or two delegates to the Congress with a consultative vote. That will probably flatter the workers and they will take up the matter enthusiastically. Do not forget that the Mensheviks will do their utmost to discredit the Congress to the workers by saying that there were no workers. This must be taken into account and we must not fail to pay serious attention to the workers being represented. The St. Petersburg workers will surely be able to col-

PRIMARY SOURCE READING 23

lect 300 roubles for two worker delegates (or perhaps some Maecenas will present this amount for such a purpose). The collecting of 5 kopeks a head will create a stir and everyone will know about it. It is extremely important. Do not fail to read this to your Committee and at the organising and agitators' meetings. Are all our organisers and agitators talking to the workers about direct links with "Vpered"?

   Greetings to you.

       Your

        Lenin

To S. I. Gusev in Petersburg [Geneva], 4th April, 1905

My dear Friend,

  You yourself wrote that they were beginning to follow and watch you. Also I have gathered from Petersburg people, who have recently arrived from the scene of action, information which completely confirms this fact. There can be no doubt about it whatsoever. I know from my own experience and from the experience of masses of comrades that possibly the most difficult thing for a revolutionary to do is to leave a dangerous place *in time*. Always, and just when it is essential to leave the work in a given place, it becomes particularly interesting and *particu-larly important*; this always seems to be the case to the person who is working. Therefore I consider it my duty to insist in the most emphatic manner that you should leave Petersburg for a time. It is absolutely necessary. No excuses whatever, no considerations for the work must delay that step. The damage from inevitable failure would be enormous, whereas the damage through leaving would be insignificant and only apparent. Appoint some young assistants for the time being, say a month or two, to take the higher positions and rest assured that the whole cause will gain considerably through this temporary loss. The young people will gain experience in doing more responsible work and any mistakes they make can soon be remedied. Whereas your ruin would entirely spoil the most important opportunities of arranging the main work for us. Once again I insistently advise you to go *at once* to the provinces for a month. There is a tremendous amount of work to be done everywhere and a guiding hand is needed. If you want (and it is essential that you should want) to leave, then it can always be arranged.

  . . . The question now is to prepare energetically for the Congress and to increase the number of delegates. As for money, do not be extravagant, save it: it will be wanted more than ever after the Congress.

INTERPRETING THE READING

Directions *Use information from the reading to answer the following questions on a separate sheet of paper.*

1. Why was getting workers to write letters and act as delegates so important to the Bolsheviks?

2. According to the first letter, Lenin is fearful of a party Congress. Why and how does increasing the number of delegates to the Congress help?

Critical Thinking

3. **Identifying Assumptions** Why was it important for Lenin's associate to disappear from St. Petersburg and why did Lenin tell him to save money for after the Congress?

4. **Synthesizing Information** The Shidlovsky Commission was organized to find out why workers and the people of St. Petersburg were discontented. Why was the election of Bolsheviks to this commission important to Lenin?

Reteaching Activity 23

War and Revolution

World War I caused human suffering and loss of life on a scale that had never before been experienced. When the war ended, the peace settlement included the payment of heavy reparations. This caused resentment and anger that eventually led to further conflict among European neighbors.

DIRECTIONS: Use the chart below to review the causes, progress, and outcomes of World War I. Complete each item by filling in the blank spaces in the columns.

World War I: Causes, Progress, and Events			
	Date	**Event**	**Description**
Causes	1882	Triple Alliance	Germany, Austria-Hungary, and Italy agree to mutual protection.
	1907		
	June 1914		
Progress on Western Front	August–September 1914		Allied forces in retreat
	September 6–10, 1914		
		stalemate	
		Verdun	
	later in 1916	Somme	
	April 1917		
	March–September 1918	Allied offensives	
	November 11, 1918		
Progress on Eastern Front	August 30, 1914		Germany decisively defeats Russian army.
			Allied attempt to open a Balkan front fails.
	mid-1915	Russian casualties at 2.5 million	
	March 1918		Russia gives up eastern Poland, Ukraine, Finland, and the Baltic provinces.
Outcome	early-1919		
	June 28, 1919		

CHAPTER 23

★ Enrichment Activity 23

Getting the Message Across

Governments often use methods of propaganda or persuasion to get their citizens to side with the government's policies at a given time, especially during times of war. Governments use the media as an easy way to distribute their message. Today these methods include television ads, print ads, or radio spots. In the era before television was invented, governments used posters to carry their propagandistic messages. During World War I, governments from both the Allies and the Central Powers used illustrated posters to rally their citizens behind their war cause.

An American wartime poster from 1917 shows a smiling, gray-haired woman standing in front of an American flag. Her arms are open and her hands are outstretched. She is depicted as a homey and maternal woman, almost grandmotherly in appearance. In the background, the artist has depicted various battle scenes in miniature. The poster reads, "Women! Help America's Sons Win the War. Buy U.S. Government Bonds."

DIRECTIONS: Answer the questions below in the space provided.

1. To whom do you think this poster is addressed? _____

   _____

2. What is the persuasive point of the poster? _____

   _____

3. Why do you think the artist drew the woman as a smiling, gray-haired, grandmotherly type? _____

   _____

4. Why do you think the woman's hands are outstretched? _____

   _____

5. To what emotions do you think the artist is trying to appeal? _____

   _____

6. Why do you think the artist has drawn the battle scenes in the background rather than the foreground? _____

   _____

7. Design your own wartime poster. Pick a clearly stated goal, such as asking volunteers to join the army or suggesting that people not waste food during the wartime shortages. Find other examples of posters in library reference books to help you. In drawing the poster, be sure that it will grab people's attention and convey your message clearly and persuasively. What is the content of your message? What persuasive techniques do you want to use? To which emotions do you wish to appeal?

World Art and Music Activity 23

George M. Cohan

Songwriter, actor, producer, and playwright, George M. Cohan had a long and successful theatrical career, beginning as a child in his parents' vaudeville act and continuing for 60 years. Many of his songs are still instantly recognizable.

DIRECTIONS: Read the passage below about this American popular song-writer. Then answer the questions in the space provided.

George Michael Cohan was born on July 3, 1878, but always celebrated his birthday on July 4, Independence Day. Cohan was the child of two successful vaudeville performers and both he and his sister joined the act, which became known as The Four Cohans.

Vaudeville was the most popular form of entertainment in the United States during the late 1800s. Vaudeville took the form of a variety show and often included between 8 and 20 short performances, or acts, in an evening. Most of these were comedy sketches or musical numbers. Child performers like the younger Cohans were common in vaudeville— they were great audience favorites. Trained animal acts or circus performers might also be on the bill. For example, W. C. Fields appeared as a juggler on the vaudeville stage before he became famous for his comedy

George M. Cohan, 1878–1942

films. Judy Garland, Jack Benny, George Burns and Gracie Allen, Buster Keaton, and Charlie Chaplin are among the many performers who, like Cohan, began their careers in vaudeville and went on to great success in Hollywood.

Cohan began writing material for The Four Cohans when he was 11. He wrote his first song at 13. In 1904 he entered a partnership with Sam H. Harris to produce and manage Broadway shows. Many of the plays they produced were Cohan's own work, including *Broadway Jones, Forty-five Minutes from Broadway,* and *Little Johnny Jones.* At the turn of the century, most musicals appearing on Broadway were European operettas featuring princesses and noblemen in mythical Balkan countries. The plots were romantic and the music consisted of lush waltzes and love duets, with the orchestrations relying heavily on violins and woodwinds. Cohan's musicals, by contrast, featured brisk, brassy marching rhythms and American subjects and characters. Some of his best-loved tunes, including "Give My Regards to Broadway" and "Yankee Doodle Dandy," were written for these shows. Their popularity paved the way for many future American playwrights, composers, and lyricists to write what became known as "Broadway musicals": *Showboat, Oklahoma!, Carousel,* and *West Side Story,* for example.

(continued)

World Art and Music Activity 23

In 1918 the United States entered World War I. Cohan's patriotic song "Over There," which exuberantly declared that the "Yanks are coming," became the most popular of the many inspirational war songs. The song reappeared to boost morale again during World War II.

With the end of the war and the beginning of the Jazz Age of the mid-1920s, Cohan's patriotic song-writing style became less popular. Only two Cohan musicals opened on Broadway during this decade; his final show, *Billie,* opened in 1928. During the 1930s, a number of Hollywood films featured Cohan songs. His play *Little Johnny Jones* was filmed in 1930. After he stopped writing musical shows, Cohan returned to acting, receiving excellent reviews for per-

formances in Eugene O'Neill's *Ah, Wilderness* and in the Rodgers and Hart musical *I'd Rather Be Right.* Cohan died in 1942.

Cohan was the subject of a 1942 musical film, *Yankee Doodle Dandy,* starring the great James Cagney, who won an Academy Award for his interpretation of the cocky, energetic, feisty, and talented Cohan. More recently, the 1968 Broadway musical *George M!* told Cohan's life story and played his songs once again. His songs are still remembered—in fact, the Cornell University fight song is sung to the tune of "Give My Regards to Broadway"! His statue stands in New York City's Times Square, in the heart of the theater district where his shows played for so many years.

Reviewing the Selection

1. List the main achievements of Cohan's career.

_____

_____

_____

2. What did a vaudeville show consist of?

_____

_____

_____

Critical Thinking

3. Identifying Central Issues Cohan had a lifelong reputation as a patriot. How do his life and work show this?

_____

_____

_____

4. Evaluating Information What do you think was Cohan's most important contribution to American musical theater? Explain.

_____

_____

_____

Glencoe

WORLD HISTORY

Chapter 23
Section Resources

SECTIONS

Guided Reading Activity 23-1

The Road to World War I

DIRECTIONS: Answer the following questions as you read Section 1.

1. What did liberals believe about European states in the early nineteenth century?

   _____

2. Name the two loose alliances of Europe's great powers.

   _____

3. How did Socialist labor movements affect strife at the start of the twentieth century?

   _____

4. What did the large size of European armies make obvious?

   _____

5. What three things may have played a role in starting World War I?

   _____

6. What assassination instigated war between Serbia and Austria-Hungary?

   _____

7. What action of Russia prompted Germany to declare war?

   _____

8. What was Germany's Schlieffen Plan?

   _____

9. By what route did Germany invade France?

   _____

10. For what official reason did Great Britain declare war on Germany?

    _____

Guided Reading Activity 23-4

End of the War

DIRECTIONS: Fill in the blanks below as you read Section 4.

1. Allied _____ on the Western Front had been badly defeated.

2. The entry of the United States into the war in 1917 gave the Allies a much-needed _____ boost.

3. The withdrawal of the Russians allowed Germany to concentrate on the _____.

4. After William II's departure, the _____ in Germany under Friedrich Ebert announced the creation of a _____ republic.

5. An attempt at revolution left the German middle class with a deep fear of _____.

6. _____ among the nations that succeeded Austria-Hungary would weaken eastern Europe for the next 80 years.

7. In January 1919, representatives of 27 victorious Allied nations met in _____ to make a final settlement of the Great War.

8. U.S. President Woodrow Wilson portrayed World War I as a people's war against "_____ and _____."

9. David Lloyd George, prime minister of _____, had a simple platform at the Peace Conference: make the Germans _____ for this dreadful war.

10. In the _____, Germany was ordered to pay reparations for all the damage to which the Allied nations had been subjected.

11. Both the German and Russian empires lost considerable _____ and the Austro-Hungarian Empire _____ altogether.

SECTION 23-4

Skills Reinforcement Activity 24

Analyzing Political Cartoons

Political cartoons are a type of drawing that is used to present editorial opinions, comment on social change, criticize current events, and point out political situations. Political cartoonists use different techniques to achieve their aims. These methods include: caricature, exaggerating a person's distinctive features; size distortion, making specific people or objects larger or smaller; symbols, using people, places, or objects to represent abstract ideas; and captions, placing words or sentences under the cartoon.

DIRECTIONS: The political cartoon below comments on communism. Study the political cartoon, and answer the questions below in the space provided.

1. What does the fire represent?

_____

_____

_____

2. Why do you think the symbol of fire was chosen?

_____

_____

_____

3. What is the fire endangering?

_____

_____

_____

The Red Peril

Frank & Marie-Therese Wood Print
Collections, Alexandria, VA

CHAPTER 24

4. What is the message of the cartoon?

_____

_____

_____

_____

_____

_____

_____

Critical Thinking Skills Activity 24 | Distinguishing Fact From Opinion

A fact is a statement that can be proved. An opinion is a personal belief. To distinguish between fact and opinion, look for statements that you can check for accuracy. Facts can be verified, or matched to those in other sources. Opinions cannot be proved; however, they gain credibility when supported by facts. A person who wants to persuade others to accept his or her opinion, but who lacks supporting facts, often appeals to the emotions instead.

DIRECTIONS: Read the following discussions, which could have taken place during the period between World War I and World War II. Then answer the questions on a separate sheet of paper.

A. United States Senate

Senator A: My fellow senators, we should not embark on any more international ventures. It is sheer folly to join this League of Nations. We would surely be drawn into another bloody European war. Do you want our young soldiers to be killed again for nothing but foolish European tribal fighting?

Senator B: Dear Senators, my colleague is correct in saying that the war was bloody. France lost 1.4 million men in the fighting; 4.3 million were wounded. In Germany 1.8 million were killed. This tragedy is why we must join the League of Nations. Had the League of Nations existed prior to the war, we could have prevented 8 million senseless deaths.

1. What are the two senators debating?

2. Which senator uses facts to make his point? What are those facts?

3. Considering that both senators could have used the same facts to support their opinions, which speech do you find more effective—the one with or without factual data? Explain your answer.

B. German Reichstag

Parliamentarian A: Thanks to the stock market crash in New York, we have now entered into another economic depression. We do not want to repeat the crisis of a decade ago when the dollar was worth 4.2 million marks! We caused this runaway inflation by printing new money to cover our debts. Now our policies are being guided by racial fear. Then and now, poor government planning has caused our problems—nothing else.

Parliamentarian B: We all know what has caused our current economic problems and those of a decade ago. Our great leader Adolf Hitler has explained it to us from the beginning. Has no one listened? The Jews are to blame for our economic depression. We must put an end to their favorable position in our society and take back what rightfully belongs to the German people. Then our economic problems will be over.

4. What facts have been presented in this debate?

5. What has caused Germany's economic problems, according to Parliamentarian A? According to Parliamentarian B?

6. Compare each speaker's use of facts in this debate.

★ HISTORY AND GEOGRAPHY ACTIVITY 24

Jews in Europe

In Berlin's Jewish Ghetto

The entrance to the Wassertorstrasse was a big stone archway, a bit of old Berlin, daubed with hammers and sickles and Nazi crosses and plastered with tattered bills which advertised auctions or crimes. It was a deep shabby cobbled street, littered with sprawling children's tears. . . .

Down in the murky pit of the courtyard, where the fog, in this clammy autumn weather, never lifted, the street singers and musicians succeeded each other in a performance which was nearly continuous. There were parties of boys with mandolins, an old man who played the concertina, and a father who sang with his little girls. . . .

Another regular visitor was the Jewish tailor and outfitter, who sold clothes of all kinds on the installment plan. He was small and gentle and very persuasive. All day long he made his rounds of the tenements in the district, collecting fifty pfennigs here, a mark there, scratching up his precarious livelihood, like a hen, from this apparently barren soil.

—From *Goodbye to Berlin* (1935) by Christopher Isherwood

On April 1, 1933, German soldiers in full uniform stood at the entrances of certain department stores and other shops, urging customers not to enter. "This is a Jewish business!" the soldiers shouted. "Remember to boycott the Jews!" Few customers dared to enter and few Jewish stores remained open. That day marked the beginning of Germany's official persecution of the Jews. Why did the German government initiate a policy of persecuting its own citizens?

After World War I, many successful Jews moved in the upper class of European society. In Germany, for example, Jews owned steel mills, railroads, shipping lines, department stores, and banks. The lives of these wealthy Jews closely resembled those of other rich Germans.

Yet for every Jew in the upper class, there were dozens of middle and working class Jews. Beginning in the late 1800s, millions of Jews fled the impoverished villages in Russia and eastern Europe. Some traveled all the way to the United States; others

Jewish tailors and small-business owners were often confined to the ghettos of central European cities because they were viewed as unwelcome competitors.

49

HISTORY AND GEOGRAPHY ACTIVITY 24 (continued)

crowded into ghettos in western European cities such as Berlin, where they eked out a living by toiling in sweatshops or peddling various wares. As their profits grew, they opened small shops and businesses.

German Jews, both rich and poor, seemed destined for success in the 1920s and 1930s. But a rising tide of jealousy and hatred brought a tragic end to their dreams—and, in millions of cases, to their lives.

Location—rural or urban, seaside or mountainside, remote or accessible—exerts a powerful influence on human activities. It can determine the kind of work people do and shape their way of living. The Jews who fled from eastern to western Europe in the late 1800s and early 1900s had to change their livelihoods. In the east they had survived primarily by farming. Because there were no farms in the western ghettos, the Jews who moved there turned to peddling and factory work. Customers were easy to find in the crowded cities, and the urban factories needed cheap labor. By adapting their lives to their new locations, the Jews were able to succeed.

APPLYING GEOGRAPHY TO HISTORY

DIRECTIONS: Answer the questions below in the space provided.

1. Why is tailoring well suited to urban locations?

   _____

2. How did location influence the lives of Jews in eastern Europe?

   _____

3. Describe how location influences human activities in your community.

   _____

Critical Thinking

4. **Making Inferences** Do you think location plays as great a role in human activities as it did 60 years ago? Use specific examples to explain your answer.

   _____

   _____

5. **Making Comparisons** Imagine you can build a new city anywhere in the United States. Which location would you choose? Why?

   _____

   _____

Activity

6. Brainstorm with your classmates a list of innovative occupational and recreational activities that might be particularly suitable for your community's location.

Name _____ Date _____ Class _____

The West Between the Wars

DIRECTIONS: Many changes took place in Europe and the United States in the years after World War I. Some of these events are listed on the time line below. Read the time line, then answer the questions that follow.

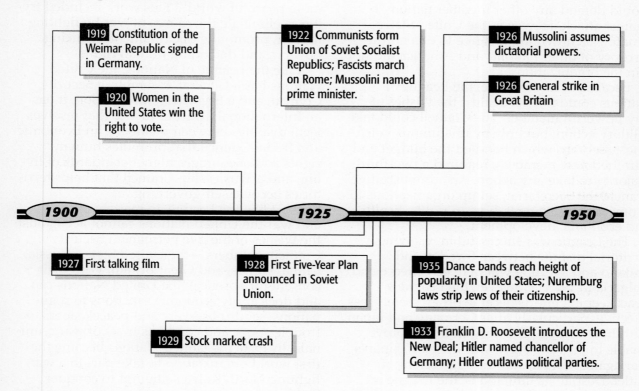

1. After which year could American women participate in choosing the President?

_____

2. How long did the Weimar Republic last? _____

3. Jewish people had no rights in Germany after which year? _____

4. **a.** In which western European country did a totalitarian leader first take control?

_____

b. Who was the leader? _____

5. **a.** What economic disaster happened in the 1920s? _____

b. In which year did this happen? _____

6. In which year did the Communists finally assume total control in Russia?

_____

7. When did the first Five-Year Plan end in the Soviet Union? _____

Linking Past and Present Activity 24

Nations United

THEN After World War I, the Paris Peace Conference adopted President Woodrow Wilson's proposal for a League of Nations. Member nations agreed to seek peaceful solutions to their conflicts and pledged that they would defend any other member nation against attack. However, the United States Senate was unwilling to agree to defend the territory of other nations, and America did not join the organization.

Because of its structure, the League of Nations could not act against the wishes of any powerful member. The Council could take military action, but only by unanimous vote. The Assembly, which handled the budget and admitted new members, required a two-thirds majority to take any action. An administrative branch, the Secretariat, set up organizations to promote disarmament, human rights, health, and economic development.

The League was successful in resolving a territorial dispute between Sweden and Finland and averting war between Greece and Bulgaria in 1925. However, the League's peacekeeping efforts became progressively less effective, particularly after Germany and Japan withdrew in 1933. The League would prove unable to prevent a civil war in Spain, Japan's war against China, and the aggressions of Hitler. Despite its limitations, the League set the pattern for how an international organization might promote peace and security.

In 1946, the League of Nations dissolved itself. The demise of the League was due mostly to a lack of organization as well as a lack of interest on the part of its more powerful nations. The functions of the League, however, were taken over by the United Nations, which was formed by the victors of World War II and initially included 50 member nations.

NOW Today, most of the world's independent nations are United Nations members. Secretary-General Kofi Annan shared the 2001 Nobel Peace Prize with the United Nations "for their work for a better organized and more peaceful world." This work included trying to eliminate the causes of war by fighting hunger, promoting disarmament, reducing poverty, and defending human rights.

Like the League of Nations, the United Nations has a General Assembly, a Security Council, and a Secretariat. In addition, it has an International Court of Justice that resolves legal disputes between members, an Economic and Social Council that promotes human rights and encourages higher standards of living, and a Trusteeship Council that helps territories become self-governing.

Also like the League, in matters of peace and war the United Nations cannot act against the wishes of the five permanent Security Council members—the United States, Russia, China, France, and Great Britain. With their consent (or absence), the United Nations can and does apply economic sanctions to rogue nations, sends observers and peacekeepers to trouble spots, and conducts trials of war criminals. In 1950, the United Nations became the first world organization to take part in a war, fighting North Korea's attempt to conquer South Korea.

Most of the United Nations' successes in peacekeeping have taken place in smaller nations and conflicts. In its mission to fight disease and hunger, as well as to promote education and technology in underdeveloped regions, the United Nations has achieved its goal on a much wider scale. Few can question the value of the United Nations as a forum in which nations can talk, vote, express opinions, and agree upon solutions.

CRITICAL THINKING

Directions: Answer the following questions on a separate sheet of paper.

1. **Making inferences:** How does the United Nations work for peace?
2. **Making comparisons:** What similarities and differences do you see between the League of Nations and the United Nations?
3. **Synthesizing information:** Think about reasons the United States might want to limit its role in the United Nations. Then do research in the library and on the Internet to identify different points of view about American support for the United Nations. Write a brief summary of your findings.

People in World History Activity 24

Profile 1

Amelia Earhart (1897–1937)

Please know that I am aware of the hazards. I want to do it because I want to do it. Women must try to do things as men have tried. When they fail, their failure must be but a challenge to others.

Amelia Earhart in a letter to her husband, the explorer George Palmer Putnam, 1937

Today, flying one's own plane is becoming a much more common practice. As recently as 50 years ago, however, flying was very unusual—especially for women. Amelia Earhart was the first woman to fly alone across the Atlantic Ocean. One of America's most celebrated aviators, she paved the way for generations of women and flyers that followed.

Few of the events in Earhart's childhood signaled the path her life would take. She was born in Kansas on July 24, 1897, the daughter of a lawyer. Educated in Pennsylvania and at New York's Columbia University, Earhart started flying as a hobby. Eager to make a difference in the world, she worked as a military nurse in Canada during World War I. After the war, she became a social worker in a poor Boston neighborhood.

Earhart became famous in 1928 when she was the first woman passenger on a transatlantic flight. She was a passenger on the *Friendship*, an airplane piloted by Wilmer Stulz. They flew from Newfoundland to Wales. This success catapulted Earhart into a career as a pilot.

Determined to justify the fame that her 1928 transatlantic crossing had brought her, Earhart flew across the Atlantic alone four years later. She also made many dramatic flights across America and played an active role in developing commercial flights.

In January 1935, Earhart became the first person to fly from Hawaii to California, the longest distance yet. Building on this amazing feat, Earhart decided in 1937 to set another record—she would be the first person to fly around the world. Accompanied by her navigator, Fred Noonan, Earhart completed nearly two-thirds of her flight before her plane vanished in the Pacific Ocean near the international date line. Many boats and airplanes searched for her, but no trace has ever been found.

There have been many theories about her disappearance. Some people think the plane crashed in the ocean and Earhart and Noonan perished. Other people think that the plane landed safely on a small island and Earhart and Noonan were taken prisoners by the Japanese, then in control of some of the islands in the area. The mystery has never been solved.

CHAPTER 24

REVIEWING THE PROFILE

Directions: Answer the following questions on a separate sheet of paper.

1. Why is Amelia Earhart famous?

2. What happened to Amelia Earhart on her 1937 flight around the world?

3. **Critical Thinking** **Drawing Conclusions.** What does Amelia Earhart represent to people?

> ## People in World History Activity 24
>
> Profile 2

Eleanor Roosevelt (1884–1962)

I loved it. I ate it up.

Eleanor Roosevelt on her work for the Navy-Marine Relief Society and the Red Cross during World War I

To those who knew Eleanor Roosevelt, her taking a spontaneous flight with Amelia Earhart from Washington, D.C., to Baltimore and back one late night after a state dinner at the White House would not be surprising. She was an independent woman with great curiosity and love of life. In her day, Eleanor Roosevelt was also one of the world's most powerful and respected women.

She was born into power and privilege. Her wealthy family taught, however, that service to the community and on behalf of those less fortunate was very important. Both of Roosevelt's parents died before she was 10, and at 15 she was sent to a boarding school in London. When Roosevelt returned to America, she taught school at a settlement house in New York City. In 1905, she married her distant cousin, Franklin Roosevelt, and the stage was set for her remarkable public career.

The social obligations of being a politician's wife bored her, but Eleanor took full advantage of the opportunities for social and political activism. She visited wounded soldiers during World War I. She joined the Women's Trade Union League and was active in the Democratic Party. She taught at a girls' school, even after Franklin became governor of New York in 1929.

Eleanor came fully into her own after Franklin was elected president in 1932. She worked tirelessly for unions, child welfare, aid to the poor, and civil rights, especially for women and African Americans. She was clever. For example, she began regular White House press conferences for women correspondents; any news agency with no women reporters hired some in order to not be scooped. In 1939, the Daughters of the American Revolution refused to let the famous African American opera singer Marian Anderson perform in Constitution Hall. Eleanor resigned her DAR membership in protest and arranged an outdoor concert for Anderson at the Lincoln Memorial; 75,000 people came.

Eleanor died in 1962, but not before taking a leading role in drafting the United Nations' Universal Declaration of Human Rights and chairing the Commission on the Status of Women under John F. Kennedy. Her entire life shows she took her family's lesson of community service to heart. Eleanor Roosevelt loved working to improve the world.

REVIEWING THE PROFILE

Directions: Answer the following questions on a separate sheet of paper.

1. What causes were most important to Eleanor Roosevelt?

2. How did Eleanor Roosevelt get news agencies to hire women reporters?

3. **Critical Thinking** **Analyzing Information.** Why did Eleanor Roosevelt hold the Marian Anderson concert at Washington's Lincoln Memorial?

PRIMARY SOURCE READING 24

Mein Kampf

Soon after he joined the obscure far-right National Socialist party, Adolf Hitler tried to use his gang of Brownshirts to seize power in Munich. The unsuccessful putsch, or small-scale revolt, that started in a Munich beer hall sent Hitler to jail. There he wrote a long political essay describing his philosophy of a "master race," his belief that the Jews were responsible for Germany's problems, and his visionary goals for himself, the Nazis, and a new German Reich, or empire. The book, titled *Mein Kampf* (My Struggle), was published in 1925 and 1927.

Guided Reading   *In this selection, read to learn Hitler's opinion of and use for propaganda.*

Ever since I have been scrutinizing political events, I have taken a tremendous interest in propagandist activity. I saw that the Socialist-Marxist organizations mastered and applied this instrument with astounding skill. And I soon realized that the correct use of propaganda is a true art which has remained practically unknown to the bourgeois parties. . . .

But it was not until the War [World War I] that it became evident what immense results could be obtained by a correct application of propaganda. . . .

For what we failed to do, the enemy did, with amazing skill and really brilliant calculation. I, myself, learned enormously from this enemy war propaganda. . . .

. . . Is propaganda a means or an end?

It is a means and must therefore be judged with regard to its end. It must consequently take a form calculated to support the aim which it serves. . . .

. . . To whom should propaganda be addressed? To the scientifically trained intelligentsia or to the less educated masses?

It must be addressed always and exclusively to the masses.

What the intelligentsia—or those who today unfortunately often go by that name—what they need is not propaganda but scientific instruction. The content of propaganda is not science any more than the object represented in a poster is art. The art of the poster lies in the designer's ability to attract the attention of the crowd by form and color. . . .

The function of propaganda does not lie in the scientific training of the individual, but in calling the masses' attention to certain facts, processes, necessities, etc., whose significance is thus for the first time placed within their field of vision.

The whole art consists in doing this so skillfully that everyone will be convinced that the fact is real, the process necessary, the necessity correct, etc. . . . [Propaganda's] effect for the most part must be aimed at the emotions and only to a very limited degree at the so-called intellect.

All propaganda must be popular and its intellectual level must be adjusted to the most limited intelligence among those it is addressed to. Consequently, the greater the mass it is intended to reach, the lower its purely intellectual level will have to be. . . .

. . . The more exclusively it takes into consideration the emotions of the masses, the more effective it will be. . . .

The receptivity of the great masses is very limited, their intelligence is small, but their power of forgetting is enormous. In consequence . . . , all effective propaganda must be limited to a very few points and must harp on these in slogans until the last member of the public understands what you want him to understand by your slogan. . . .

For instance, it was absolutely wrong to make the enemy ridiculous, as the Austrian and German comic papers did. It was absolutely wrong because actual contact with an enemy soldier was bound to arouse an entirely different conviction, and the results were devastating; for now the German soldier . . . felt himself swindled by his propaganda service. His desire to

PRIMARY SOURCE READING 24

fight, or even to stand firm, was not strengthened, but the opposite occurred. His courage flagged.

By contrast, the war propaganda of the [British] and Americans was psychologically sound. By representing the Germans to their own people as barbarians and Huns, they prepared the individual soldier for the terrors of war, and thus helped to preserve him from disappointments. . . . It . . . reinforced his faith in the truth of his government's assertions, while on the other hand it increased his rage and hatred against the vile enemy. . . .

And so the [British] soldier could never feel that he had been misinformed by his own countrymen. . . .

It was absolutely wrong [for the German government] to discuss war-guilt from the standpoint that Germany alone could not be held responsible for the outbreak of the catastrophe; it would have been correct to load every bit of the blame on the shoulders of the enemy. . . .

. . . As soon as our own propaganda admits so much as a glimmer of right on the other side, the foundation for doubt in our own right has been laid. The masses are then in no position to distinguish where foreign injustice ends and our own begins. . . .

[British] propagandists understood all this most brilliantly—and acted accordingly. They made no half statements that might have given rise to doubts. . . .

. . . The most brilliant propagandist technique will yield no success unless one fundamental principle is borne in mind constantly and with unflagging attention. It must confine itself to a few points and repeat them over and over. . . .

INTERPRETING THE READING

Directions *Use information from the reading to answer the following questions. If necessary, use a separate sheet of paper.*

1. From what Hitler says and your own study of World War I, what was the aim of Allied propaganda? Why does Hitler believe this was more effective than the German propaganda?

   _____

2. According to Hitler, to whom must propaganda be directed? Why?

   _____

3. Briefly describe Hitler's recommended propaganda technique.

   _____

4. Why does Hitler argue that propaganda must be completely one-sided?

   _____

Critical Thinking

5. **Demonstrating Reasoned Judgment** In your opinion, do Hitler's ideas about propaganda apply today in advertising and political campaigning? If so, how?

   _____

   _____

   _____

Reteaching Activity 24

The West Between the Wars

The postwar era saw dramatic changes and innovations in lifestyles, science and technology, and the arts. At the same time, many countries struggled under the strain of war debts and a worldwide depression. While the United States, France, and Great Britain retained their democratic structure, totalitarian governments emerged in Germany, Italy, and the Soviet Union. Use the chart below to review some post–World War I cultural, economic, and political developments in the United States, Great Britain, France, Italy, Germany, and the Soviet Union.

DIRECTIONS: Copy the chart below onto a separate sheet of paper. Then read the items in the list below and write them in the appropriate spaces in the chart. Some items belong in more than one space. The chart has been started for you.

- industrial and agricultural workers strike
- art reflects state goals
- *Quo Vadis*
- Conservatives replace Labour Party
- Stalin and Five-Year Plan
- huge war debts
- poet Paul Valéry
- Popular Front
- Treaty of Locarno
- Lenin and NEP

- drought causes famine
- coalition government
- creation of Weimar Republic
- *Birth of a Nation*
- no longer world's trade leader
- government purges
- Roosevelt and the New Deal
- initial economic boom
- Hannah Höch uses photomontage
- Hermann Hesse

- *Kraft durch Freude*
- economy near ruin
- John Maynard Keynes
- 1929 stock market crash sets off worldwide depression
- French New Deal
- rise of fascism and Mussolini
- use of radios increases
- rise of Nazism and Hitler
- Works Progress Administration
- high unemployment

Changes in the Postwar Era

Country	Cultural Developments	Economic Developments	Political Developments
United States		initial economic boom	
Great Britain			
France		huge war debts	coalition government
Italy		huge war debts	
Germany			Treaty of Locarno
Soviet Union			

★ Enrichment Activity 24

No Laughing Matter: Interpreting Political Cartoons

Whether you are reading today's newspaper or researching history, political cartoons can help you understand the arguments surrounding an issue. Cartoonists illustrate their point of view through satirical drawings rather than lengthy editorials. Sometimes their cartoons depict actual people involved in an issue; other times the characters symbolize ideas, groups, or nations.

"Interrupting the Ceremony" copyrighted © Chicago Tribune Company. All rights reserved. Used with permission.

DIRECTIONS: Look at the political cartoon and answer the questions in the space provided.

1. What type of ceremony is being depicted by the cartoon?_____
   _____
   _____

2. Who is the bearded man, and what does he represent?_____
   _____

3. What does the woman represent? _____
   _____
   _____

4. What does the ceremony symbolize? ____
   _____
   _____

5. What is interrupting the ceremony?_____
   _____

6. Why is the ceremony being interrupted? _____
   _____

7. Around what year might this cartoon have appeared? _____
   _____

8. Where do you think the cartoonist stands on this issue? Why do you think so?_____
   _____
   _____
   _____

World Art and Music Activity 24

Dada

World War I resulted in mass killing on a scale unknown before, leading to despair and the belief that the traditions of Western culture were at fault. The French artist Marcel Duchamp and other artists and writers who shared this attitude launched a movement called Dada or Dadaism. The term means "hobbyhorse" in French and was reportedly selected at random from a dictionary. Its purpose was to inform the public that all established values were meaningless in light of World War I.

DIRECTIONS: Read the following passage about Dada, then answer the questions in the space provided.

Dada art was a reaction to existing culture, particularly in art. Art that was carefully constructed and thought out, even impressionistic and realistic art, was considered to be a trait of the culture that led to World War I. Dada artists in the United States and western Europe instead relied on chance and imagination to create their works. Marcel Duchamp would take a ready-made item, such as a metal wine rack, attach his name to it, and exhibit it as a work of art.

Dada artists took existing forms of art and added the elements of chance and imagination. Hans Arp, for example, created a new form of collage in which he arranged colored pieces of paper shaped by tearing rather than by cutting and dropped them on a larger sheet to create his works. German Dadaist Max Ernst composed collages using pieces of illustrations of machinery.

Dada art was a negative reaction to traditional art. It was anti-art and it was meant to assault the senses.

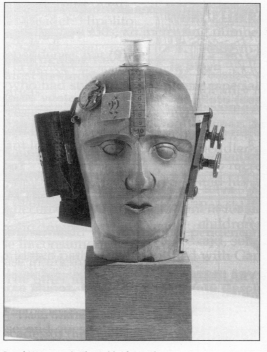

Raoul Hausmann's *The Spirit of Our Times*

But there was also liberation from unleashing the creative mind.

In Zurich, Jean Arp and Sophie Taeuber created nonfigurative drawings, watercolors, and embroideries dominated by horizontal and vertical structures. Arp declared that they eliminated "everything that was merely a matter of entertainment or taste from our investigations; even the personal touch struck us as useless and embarrassing, for it was the emanation of a dead and rigid world." They used embroidering, weaving, painting, and gluing static geometric forms to create their impersonal constructions. They were typical of Dadaists who could not be bound to any one technique or type of expression; they mixed traditional forms of expression to oppose the traditional forms of art.

German Dadaist Raoul Hausmann's *The Spirit of Our Times* is a combination of both sculpture and collage. Hausmann started with the theory that people have no personality and that their face is simply

(continued)

> ## World Art and Music Activity 24

an image created at the hairdresser's. So he used a hairdressers' practice dummy head as the base for this piece. He added items to the head. He said of this work that "the average man's only capacities are the ones that chance has stuck him with—you might say the ones that chance has stuck onto his skull; his brain is empty." So Hausmann got a head and started sticking things on it. He used a collapsible cup, a purse, a little jewel case, a typography cylinder, and a pipe stem inside the case. On the left side he changed materials and attached a bronze compo-

nent from an old camera to a ruler. He added a piece of white cardboard with the number "22" marked on it, he said because "the spirit of our times was obviously numerical."

Literary and performance art also had a Dadaist form. Poetry readings might consist of poems of sheer nonsense words repeated many times. Performances might be improvised as they were performed.

Dadaism had a relatively brief life, from about 1916 to 1922. However, it laid the groundwork for surrealism, a form of art that has endured.

Reviewing the Selection

1. What was the purpose of Dadaist art?

_____

_____

_____

2. What are the characteristics of Dadaist art?

_____

_____

_____

Critical Thinking

3. **Making Comparisons** Compare a form of modern artistic expression, such as rap songs or performance "happenings," with Dada art.

_____

_____

_____

4. **Determining Cause and Effect** Dada was a reaction to World War I. Describe another form of artistic expression that has resulted from events in the last half of the twentieth century.

_____

_____

_____

_____

_____

Using an Electronic Spreadsheet

A spreadsheet is an electronic worksheet that can manage numbers quickly and easily. All spreadsheets follow a basic design of rows and columns. Each column is assigned a letter, and each row is assigned a number. Each point where a column and row intersect is called a cell. The cell's position on the spreadsheet is labeled according to its corresponding column and row, so A1 is column A, row 1. Spreadsheets use formulas to calculate numbers. To create a formula, highlight the cell you want the results in, and then build the formula, step by step.

DIRECTIONS: Use the information in the table below to create your own electronic spreadsheet and calculate the balance of trade for each of these Latin American countries. Then answer the questions on a separate sheet of paper. Your spreadsheet should have seven columns and six rows.

Value of Latin American Imports and Exports, 1989 and 1999 (in billions of dollars)				
Country	**1989 Import Value**	**1989 Export Value**	**1999 Import Value**	**1999 Export Value**
Argentina	$1.4	$1.0	$2.6	$4.9
Brazil	$2.7	$4.8	$11.3	$13.2
Chile	$1.3	$0.7	$2.9	$3.1
Peru	$0.8	$0.6	$1.9	$1.7
Mexico	$27.2	$24.9	$109.7	$86.9

1. Enter the data from the table into your spreadsheet.

2. In Column D (the fourth column), place the heading "1989 Balance of Trade" in the first cell of the column. Then calculate the 1989 balance of trade for each country and enter it into the spreadsheet.

3. Enter the data from the last two columns of the chart into Columns E and F of the spreadsheet. In Column G, place the heading "1999 Balance of Trade" in the first cell. Then calculate the 1999 balance of trade for each country and enter it into the spreadsheet.

4. What formula did you use to calculate the balance of trade for each country? How would you express that formula in spreadsheet terms?

5. Which country in 1989 has a favorable balance of trade? Which countries in 1999 have a favorable balance of trade?

6. Based on the balance of trade, which country has experienced the most economic difficulty? Give a reason for your answer.

Critical Thinking Skills Activity 25 | Predicting Consequences

Every action or decision produces some kind of consequence. Statements of foreign policy are decisions that produce consequences in the way the United States reacts to events in other countries. Examining statements of foreign policy can allow you to predict what those reactions will be.

DIRECTIONS: Look at the flowcharts below. Then complete the activities on a separate sheet of paper.

CHAPTER 25

| In 1904, Theodore Roosevelt announced that although the United States had no desire to seize territory in Latin America, "chronic wrongdoing" by any Latin American nation would justify intervention by the United States. | → | Nicaraguans revolted against American-backed Adolfo Díaz in 1912. | → | 2,500 U.S. Marines were sent to Nicaragua. |

1. What decision did President Theodore Roosevelt make about U.S. foreign policy toward Latin America in 1904?

2. How did this decision affect the reaction of the U.S. government to events in Nicaragua in 1912?

3. How would you predict this reaction might have affected public opinion toward the United States in Nicaragua?

| In his first inaugural address in 1933, President Franklin D. Roosevelt said that he would dedicate the nation "to the policy of the good neighbor—the neighbor who resolutely respects himself and, because he does so, respects the rights of others—the neighbor who respects his obligations and respects the sanctity of his agreements in and with a world of neighbors." | → | Lázaro Cárdenas nationalizes American-owned oil wells. | → |  |

4. What was Franklin D. Roosevelt's policy toward Latin America?

5. What event or action occurred in Mexico after Roosevelt's announcement of his new policy?

6. Listed below are three possible reactions Roosevelt might have had to Cárdenas's action. Choose the one that seems most likely and write the letter in the blank box of the flowchart. Explain your answer.
  a. U.S. Marines invade Mexico to force return of oil wells.
  b. The United States pressures Mexico to compensate oil companies for the wells.
  c. The United States does nothing.

★ HISTORY AND GEOGRAPHY ACTIVITY 25

Peoples of Iraq

In 1920, the League of Nations mandated the creation of the country of Iraq under British administration. The borders for this new nation were drafted by British civil servants, with no representation by the peoples then inhabiting the region. But did this new nation really represent one people?

When the British established Iraq, they incorporated the people then living in the area into four main geographic regions. To the west of the Euphrates River, Bedouin nomads inhabited the stony plain that edges the Syrian Desert. Bedouin clans and the Madan (Marsh Arabs) lived east of the river in the Alluvial Plains below Baghdad. Tribal Arab plainsmen of the Shammar confederacy inhabited the northern uplands. The Kurds made their home in the steppes and mountains of the northern highlands north of Mosul and Kirkuk.

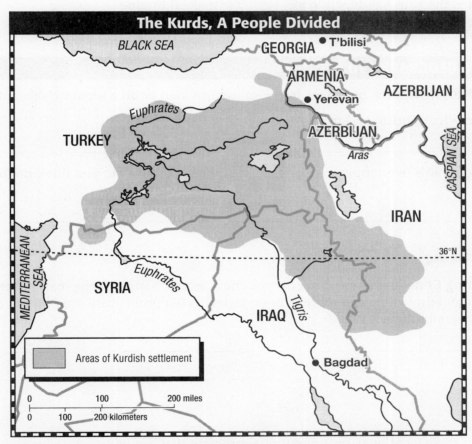

The Kurds, A People Divided

The political boundaries of Iraq bear little relationship to ethnic boundaries. Note that the mountainous region where the Kurdish people live is split between five countries. The Kurds, who used to herd livestock freely across these lands, are now restricted in their movements. These restrictions have isolated Kurds across the border from one another and forced the Kurds to alter their traditional semi-nomadic ways.

HISTORY AND GEOGRAPHY ACTIVITY 25 (continued)

The Kurdish people have a distinct identity. They are neither Arabic nor Semitic, they have their own Aryan language with many Persian words, and, while the majority of Iraqis are Shiite Muslims, the majority of Kurds belong to the Sunni Muslim sect.

For centuries, the Kurds have struggled for independence, seeking to establish a nation in the mountainous region that lies between Iraq, Iran, Syria, Armenia, and Turkey. A 1920 treaty with the Ottoman sultanate would have established a separate Kurdistan, but the Ottoman Empire collapsed, leaving the treaty that would have granted the Kurds independence among the rubble.

Geographic areas may belong to more than one region. The Kurds of Iraq, for example, belongs to both the Kurdish ethnic group and to the political region called Iraq. The map on the previous page shows how the regions overlap.

Your community may also belong to overlapping regions. Your climatic region, for example, probably overlaps your political, economic, and vegetation regions. Other overlapping regions may include those based on population or physical features. The particular combination of regions of which your community is a part helps make it unique.

APPLYING GEOGRAPHY TO HISTORY

DIRECTIONS: Answer the questions in the space provided or on a separate sheet of paper.

1. Explain why political and tribal regions overlap in Iraq.

   _____

2. Based on Iraq's overlapping regions, what kinds of conflicts do you think might exist there?

   _____

Critical Thinking

3. **Predicting Consequences** What do you think would happen if the map of the Middle East were redrawn to reflect ethnic boundaries? What problems would be solved? What problems might arise? Why?

   _____

   _____

Activity

4. Identify a local, national, or international problem that can be traced to overlapping regions. Draw a map that shows the existing regions; then draw a revised map that shows how the problem could be solved. Write a few sentences to explain your revisions.

Time Line Activity 25

Nationalism Around the World

Background — Hope for a new, more civilized world after World War I brought new borders and new expressions of nationalism.

DIRECTIONS: The time line below lists several important events of this "time between the wars." Read and list them, then decide whether each event was a *result* of emerging nationalist ideas or a *cause* of greater nationalism. Be prepared to explain your choices.

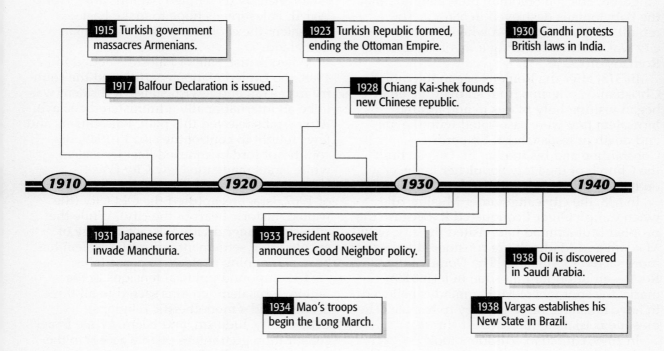

1915 Turkish government massacres Armenians.

1917 Balfour Declaration is issued.

1923 Turkish Republic formed, ending the Ottoman Empire.

1928 Chiang Kai-shek founds new Chinese republic.

1930 Gandhi protests British laws in India.

1910   1920   1930   1940

1931 Japanese forces invade Manchuria.

1933 President Roosevelt announces Good Neighbor policy.

1934 Mao's troops begin the Long March.

1938 Oil is discovered in Saudi Arabia.

1938 Vargas establishes his New State in Brazil.

Causes and Results of Nationalism		
Event	**Cause(√)**	**Result(√)**

Linking Past and Present Activity 25

Jerusalem

THEN The first known name given to Jerusalem was Ur Salem—the City of Peace. Despite its name, few cities have been the site of so much conflict.

First occupied in 4000 B.C., Ur Salem was a Canaanite stronghold when the Jewish king David conquered it around 1000 B.C. David walled the city and made it the capital of his kingdom. His son Solomon built a temple that the Babylonians destroyed in 586 B.C. The rebuilt temple was ruined when much of the city was destroyed during a revolt against the Romans in 132 to 135.

In 313, after the Romans began tolerating Christianity, pilgrims from all over the empire began visiting holy places in and around Jerusalem that were associated with the life and death of Jesus Christ. Emperor Constantine and his mother St. Helena built the Church of the Holy Sepulcher in the city on the site of Christ's tomb.

In 638, the city came under Muslim rule when Caliph Omar I conquered it. Because the prophet Muhammad had visited the city, only Makkah and Madinah are considered to be more sacred to Muslims. The Dome of the Rock—an important mosque in Jerusalem—marks the spot where Muhammad is believed to have taken his night journey to heaven. The mosque is Islam's third holiest shrine.

In 1099, Christian crusaders took Jerusalem, but a victory by Saladin in 1187 returned the city to Muslim control. In 1517, the city became part of the Ottoman Empire and remained so until its capture by the British during World War I.

NOW Today, Jerusalem is claimed by both Israelis and Palestinians and remains important to the political and religious identities of both groups of people. Control of the city remains a critical issue in the ongoing conflict that exists between Israelis and Palestinians.

The state of Israel claims the entire city as the capital of the Jewish homeland, as it was established by the United Nations after World War II. Palestinians hope to make East Jerusalem the capital of a new Palestinian homeland.

When British rule of Palestine ended in 1948, the United Nations partitioned the country into Arab and Jewish states. Jerusalem was to be an internationally administered enclave. After Arabs rejected this plan, Palestinians and Jews fought to control the city. In 1949, the country of Jordan annexed East Jerusalem, while Israel made the New City (West Jerusalem) its capital. During the Six Day War of 1967, Israel recaptured the Old City (the walled, historic heart of the city). While the city is no longer divided, Israel's policy of encouraging settlement in East Jerusalem has been an ongoing obstacle to peace talks.

To compound political tensions in the region, Jerusalem remains sacred to all three of the world's monotheistic religions: Christianity, Judaism, and Islam. While Israel's constitution guarantees people access to the sacred sites of all religions, many Muslims claim that Temple Mount is sacred to their faith alone. Violent protests have been sparked by Jewish plans to build a third temple on the Mount. Muslims seek to expand al-Aqsa Mosque, also on Temple Mount, into the largest mosque in the Middle East.

CRITICAL THINKING

Directions: Answer the following questions on a separate sheet of paper.

1. **Making inferences:** Why is Jerusalem significant to Muslims, Christians, and Jews?
2. **Drawing conclusions:** Why do some consider the future of Jerusalem to be the key to peace in the Middle East?

3. **Synthesizing information:** Do research in the library and on the Internet to find out about recent developments in the conflict over Jerusalem. Choose one recent event, write a brief summary of the event, and explain its impact on Jerusalem's history.

> ## People in World History Activity 25
>
> ### Profile 1

Chaim Weizmann (1874–1952)

Chaim Weizmann was born in Russia, the third of 15 children. His family emphasized education. He left Russia to attend university because the Russian universities had quota restrictions for admitting Jewish students. He earned a PhD in chemistry and became a renowned chemist.

From childhood Weizmann also believed that the Jewish people should return to their homeland in Palestine (the Holy Land) and establish a Jewish state. Thus Weizmann easily took to Zionism, which began in its modern form with Theodor Herzl. Zionism's mission was to found a state for the scattered Jewish people. The movement is called Zionism after Zion, one of the hills in Jerusalem. It is believed King David established the capital there, and the word *Zion* occurs frequently in the Old Testament as a name for Jerusalem.

Weizmann first joined the Zionist movement as head of the Young Zionists, who opposed Herzl's willingness to accept the British proposal of founding the Jewish state in an unpopulated section of Uganda. For Weizmann the homeland would have to be in Palestine. Later he played a crucial role in negotiating the Balfour Declaration. In 1920, Weizmann became head of the

World Zionist Organization. During the 1920s, he traveled throughout the world preaching Zionism and raising money for the cause at mass rallies.

By the 1930s, however, factions within the Zionist movement wanted Weizmann out because he was negotiating with the British, who had backed off their commitment to a Jewish national homeland. He supported the 1937 British recommendation to divide Palestine in half, making one part a Jewish state and the other an Arab state. The proposal failed, but his support again angered the radical Zionists.

After World War II, Weizmann's opposition to the Jewish guerrilla campaign against the British cost him the world Zionist presidency. As the crowning achievement of his life, however, when the Jewish homeland—Israel—was finally established, Weizmann was elected its first president.

CHAPTER 25

REVIEWING THE PROFILE

Directions: Answer the following questions on a separate sheet of paper.

1. Why was the movement to found a Jewish national homeland called Zionism?

2. What was the crowning achievement of Chaim Weizmann's life?

3. **Critical Thinking Recognizing Bias.** Theodor Herzl believed that the question of the Jewish national homeland should be settled "by the civilized nations of the world in council." He had in mind the United States and the European nations. Does this statement have a bias? If so, why? If not, why not?

People in World History Activity **25**

Profile 2

Haile Selassie (1892–1975)

> *Apart from the Kingdom of God, there is not on this earth any nation that is higher than any other.*
>
> Haile Selassie in a speech delivered to
> the League of Nations, June 30, 1936

Said to be descended from the Queen of Sheba and King Solomon, Haile Selassie was emperor of Ethiopia from 1930 to 1974. He introduced many economic and social reforms and led Ethiopia into the League of Nations and the United Nations.

Named Tafari Makonnen at birth, he was born into a prominent political family. When he was 18 years old, Tafari took over his father's job of governor of Harar. The following year, he married Wayzaro Menen, Emperor Menelik II's great-granddaughter.

When the emperor died in 1913, his grandson Lij Yasu became the new ruler. Lij Yasu's close ties to Islam alienated Ethiopia's Christian majority. Supported by the Christian leaders, Tafari deposed the new emperor in 1916, and Menelik's daughter Zauditu became empress. Tafari was then named the regent and heir to the throne.

For the next 12 years Tafari solidified his power, subduing a number of rebellions and creating his own army. He set up schools across Ethiopia and sent promising young scholars abroad to study. In 1923, he had Ethiopia admitted to the League of Nations. He freed enslaved Ethiopians the

following year and brought foreign advisers to the country to help with technical and economic matters.

In 1928, Tafari took the title *Negus* (king). He was crowned emperor two years later, when Zauditu died. He took the title Haile Selassie, which means "Power of the Trinity." His other titles included Lion of Judah, Elect of God, and King of Kings of Ethiopia.

In 1935 Italy invaded Ethiopia, and Haile Selassie was forced into exile. In a famous speech before the League of Nations in 1936, he asked the league to impose military sanctions on Italy. His appeal was denied, and Haile Selassie was forced into exile in England. In 1941, with the help of the British and an army of Ethiopian exiles, he defeated the Italians.

Although Haile Selassie passed many important reforms, including universal suffrage, Ethiopia suffered from widespread unemployment, inflation, and starvation. These problems created great anger. As a result, Haile Selassie was deposed by the army in 1974 and put under house arrest. He died the following year.

REVIEWING THE PROFILE

Directions: Answer the following questions on a separate sheet of paper.

1. How did Selassie become emperor of Ethiopia?

2. Why was Selassie deposed?

3. **Critical Thinking** **Making Inferences.** What did Selassie mean when he said, "there is not . . . any nation that is higher than any other"? To what political situation was he referring?

PRIMARY SOURCE READING 25

The Sykes-Picot Agreement: 1916

World War I provided Arab nationalists, with the support of the British, the opportunity to gain independence from Ottoman rule. The British and French governments then agreed to create a number of mandates supervised by the League of Nations. The Sykes-Picot Agreement was one such agreement.

Guided Reading *In this selection, read to learn about some of the agreements made between Britain and France regarding the Arab states.*

It is accordingly understood between the French and British governments:

That France and Great Britain are prepared to recognize and protect an independent Arab states or a confederation of Arab states (a) and (b) marked on the annexed map, under the suzerainty of an Arab chief. That in area (a) France, and in area (b) Great Britain, shall have priority of right of enterprise and local loans. That in area (a) France, and in area (b) Great Britain, shall alone supply advisers or foreign functionaries at the request of the Arab state or confederation of Arab states.

That in the blue area France, and in the red area Great Britain, shall be allowed to establish such direct or indirect administration or control as they desire and as they may think fit to arrange with the Arab state or confederation of Arab states.

That in the brown area there shall be established an international administration, the form of which is to be decided upon after consultation with Russia, and subsequently in consultation with the other Allies, and the representatives of the sheriff of [Makkah].

That Great Britain be accorded (1) the ports of Haifa and Acre, (2) guarantee of a given supply of water from the Tigres and Euphrates in area (a) for area (b). His majesty's government, on their part, undertake that they will at no time enter into negotiations for the cession of Cyprus to any third power without the previous consent of the French government.

That in area (a) the Baghdad railway shall not be extended southwards beyond Mosul, and in area (b) northwards beyond Samarra, until a railway connecting Baghdad and Aleppo via

the Euphrates Valley has been completed, and then only with the concurrence of the two governments.

That Great Britain has the right to build, administer, and be sole owner of a railway connecting Haifa with area (b), and shall have a perpetual right to transport troops along such a line at all times. It is to be understood by both governments that this railway is to facilitate the connection of Baghdad with Haifa by rail, and it is further understood that, if the engineering difficulties and expense entailed by keeping this connecting line in the brown area only make the project unfeasible, that the French government shall be prepared to consider that the line in question may also traverse the Polgon Banias Keis Marib Salkhad tell Otsda Mesmie before reaching area (b).

For a period of twenty years the existing Turkish customs tariff shall remain in force throughout the whole of the blue and red areas, as well as in areas (a) and (b), and no increase in the rates of duty or conversions from ad valorem to specific rates shall be made except by agreement between the two powers.

There shall be no interior customs barriers between any of the above mentioned areas. The customs duties leviable on goods destined for the interior shall be collected at the port of entry and handed over to the administration of the area of destination.

It shall be agreed that the French government will at no time enter into any negotiations for the cession of their rights and will not cede such rights in the blue area to any third power, except the Arab state or confederation of Arab states, without the previous agreement of his majesty's

PRIMARY SOURCE READING 25

government, who, on their part, will give a similar undertaking to the French government regarding the red area.

The British and French government, as the protectors of the Arab state, shall agree that they will not themselves acquire and will not consent to a third power acquiring territorial possessions in the Arabian Peninsula, nor consent to a third power installing a naval base either on the east coast, or on the islands, of the Red Sea. This, however, shall not prevent such adjustment of the Aden frontier as may be necessary in consequence of recent Turkish aggression.

The negotiations with the Arabs as to the boundaries of the Arab states shall be continued through the same channel as heretofore on behalf of the two powers.

The negotiations with the Arabs as to the boundaries of the Arab states shall be continued through the same channel as heretofore on behalf of the two powers.

It is agreed that measures to control the importation of arms into the Arab territories will be considered by the two governments.

I have further the honor to state that, in order to make the agreement complete, his majesty's government are proposing to the Russian government to exchange notes analogous to those exchanged by the latter and your excellency's government on the 26th April last. Copies of these notes will be communicated to your excellency as soon as exchanged. I would also venture to remind your excellency that the conclusion of the present agreement raises, for practical consideration, the question of claims of Italy to a share in any partition or rearrangement of Turkey in Asia, as formulated in article 9 of the agreement of the 26th April, 1915, between Italy and the Allies.

His majesty's government further consider that the Japanese government should be informed of the arrangements now concluded.

INTERPRETING THE READING

Directions *Use information from the reading to answer the following questions. If necessary, use a separate sheet of paper.*

1. Describe the relationship between Britain and France as suggested by the Sykes-Picot Agreement.

_____

2. What agreements were outlined regarding the existing Turkish customs tariffs?

_____

Critical Thinking

3. **Explain** Why do you think Britain and France wanted the League of Nations to supervise the newly divided Arab territories?

_____

_____

Reteaching Activity 25

Nationalism Around the World

Around the globe, people struggled to break traditional political power structures after the end of World War I. In Asia, the Ottoman Empire crumbled. Africans and Latin Americans sought to break colonial ties and form new nations.

DIRECTIONS: Each of the five sentences in the outline below refers to a nationalist struggle that occurred between 1919 and 1939. Add details to each sentence by completing the outline with statements from the following list.

- Good Neighbor policy keeps U.S. troops from entering Mexico.
- Policies help Brazil become Latin America's chief industrial power.
- Forms alliance with Communist Party.
- Argues that British rule was destroying the traditional culture of the peoples of Africa.

- Vargas establishes a Fascist-like state in Brazil.
- Creates dynasty called Pahlavi.
- Educated in Great Britain.
- Establishes PEMEX to run the oil industry.
- Leads movement that overthrows the shah.
- Needs the expertise of the Soviet Union.

I. Reza Khan wants to reduce foreign influences in Iran.

　A. _____

　B. _____

II. Jomo Kenyatta becomes leader of the nationalist movement in Kenya.

　A. _____

　B. _____

III. Sun Yat-sen's Nationalist Party competes for right to rule China.

　A. _____

　B. _____

IV. Lázaro Cárdenas seizes the oil wells in Mexico from foreign control.

　A. _____

　B. _____

V. Getúlio Vargas makes himself a dictator.

　A. _____

　B. _____

★ Enrichment Activity 25

Salt and Satyagraha

In 1930, when Gandhi returned to political life, *The New York Times* wrote, "In [Britain] the India crisis is not yet a topic of general conversation outside of political groups, and in India itself millions of people know nothing about it." Gandhi faced the problem of bringing the Indian struggle for independence to the attention of the world. He decided to do this through a protest on the salt tax.

> The [salt] tax constitutes . . . therefore the most inhuman poll tax that the ingenuity of man can devise. The . . . tax [raises the price by as much as] 2,400 [percent] [over the wholesale] price! What this means to the poor can hardly be imagined by us. Salt production like cotton growing has been centralized for the sake of sustaining the inhuman monopoly. . . . The necessary consequence of salt monopoly was the . . . closing down of salt works in thousands of places where the poor people manufactured their own salt.
>
> The illegality is in a Government that steals the people's salt and makes them pay heavily for the stolen article. The people, when they become conscious of their power, will have every right to take possession of what belongs to them.
>
> –From *Gandhi Wields the Weapon of Moral Power*
> by Gene Sharp, copyright © 1960 by The Nevajivan Trust.

DIRECTIONS: Answer the questions below in the space provided.

1. Write a one-sentence summary of Gandhi's explanation. _____
    _____

2. Explain why Gandhi chose the salt tax as the focus of his campaign. _____
    _____

3. In another statement, Gandhi said, "The salt tax oppresses all alike—Hindu, [Muslim], Parsee, Christian, Jew." Why would this aspect of the tax make it a good focus for Gandhi's campaign? _____
    _____

4. What, according to Gandhi, made the tax on salt illegal? _____
    _____

5. The legitimacy of the salt tax campaign was strengthened by the fact that many British officials had also criticized the salt tax as unfair. Thus Gandhi and others were able to quote British officials in their campaigns against the tax. How might this have affected the initial response of the British government to the campaign? _____
    _____
    _____

6. The word *satyagraha* means "truth force." How was the force of truth used in the campaign against the salt tax? _____
    _____

CHAPTER 25

World Art and Music Activity 25

Diego Rivera

The early twentieth century was a time of political and social unrest in Mexico. One particular problem faced by the Mexican people was *peonage*. Poor Mexicans ("peons") who worked a landlord's farm were forced into debt, a debt that extended to their descendants if it remained unpaid—as it usually did. This indentured servitude was outlawed in 1915, but it continued until 1936. In that year, President Cárdenas instituted the *ejido*. This took land away from the landlords and put it into the hands of the government, which paid for improvements, seeds, and so on. On these new communal farms, laborers were paid for their work.

DIRECTIONS: Read the passage below about one socially conscious Mexican artist. Then answer the questions in the space provided.

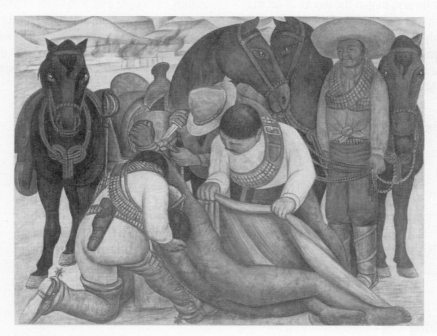

Diego Rivera, *Liberation of the Peon* (1931)

Diego Rivera (1886–1957) always wanted to be a painter, and, along with his academic pursuits, he persuaded his parents to let him study art. He completed his first works when he was still a teenager and used the money from their sale to travel to Spain to study art with professionals. Rivera studied in Spain from 1907 to 1909 and then in Paris from 1912 to 1921, selling enough of his work to support himself. Yet even after 17 years he never felt at home: he was Mexican and Mexico was where his heart and soul were.

Almost immediately upon his return, Rivera was commissioned by the Mexican government to paint a mural for the auditorium of the National Preparatory School. Its title was *Creation* and it showed Mexican figures representing primal energy, man, woman, knowledge, tragedy, strength, science, charity, and

(continued)

World Art and Music Activity 25

other elements. Rivera had not yet found the subject matter that was right for him, though he had found his style. He used vivid colors: yellows, blues, golds, greens, whites, and reds. He reinterpreted shapes, such as the use of the curve, which would stand out in every one of his works. A bent arm for Rivera is round, not L-shaped; from neck to knee of a seated figure is one long arc. Finally, Rivera believed that art belonged to the people and that its most appropriate place was on the walls of public buildings, where everyone could experience it.

In 1922 Rivera joined the Communist Party, believing that its theories of equal distribution of resources and wealth would improve the life of Mexico's peasants. At this time he also began the works of art that he is most known for: the history of the Mexican worker in his daily life and his struggle for freedom, equality, and dignity.

In 1923 Rivera began his first major work: 124 frescoes for the Ministry of Education illustrating the cultural and work life of the Mexican people. Rivera considered this an uplifting work that proclaimed the glorious soul of Mexico and Mexicans. At the same time he was working on a series of frescoes for the Agricultural College. The theme of these murals could be summed up by the words of Zapata, which Rivera placed over the mural: "Here it is taught to exploit the land but not the man." Rivera felt strongly that all the land belonged to the people.

From 1949 until 1955, Rivera worked on the walls of the National Palace in Mexico City. Here he communicated the epic story of his people, from conquest to the present and even into the future—the utopia of his dreams. The mural contained thousands of people and hundreds of stories, in bold hues from Rivera's trademark palette. One historian has said that the completed work "was not a painting but a world on a wall"—a world that Rivera loved passionately and that he honored in every work he created.

Reviewing the Selection

1. Where are some of Diego Rivera's most important works located?

_____

2. What subject did most of his work portray?

_____

_____

3. Why did Rivera specialize in murals on public buildings?

_____

_____

Critical Thinking

4. Identifying Central Issues *Liberation of the Peon* shows a group of soldiers covering a dead farmer in a blanket. In the background the hacienda burns; the landowner responsible for the peon's death has been punished. From what things do you think the peon is being liberated?

_____

_____

5. Drawing Conclusions Rivera considered his art happy, even when it told of struggle and heartache. What in his work supports his belief?

_____

_____

Skills Reinforcement Activity 26

Synthesizing Information

When you synthesize information, you combine information you have obtained from several sources. In doing research, you should not rely on only one source.

It is better to find a variety of sources, even ones that show opposing points of view, in order to see all sides of an issue.

DIRECTIONS: Read the two excerpts below regarding the use of the atomic bomb by the United States in 1945. Then answer the questions below on a separate sheet of paper.

From the Interim Committee on Military Use of the Atomic Bomb, 1945

It was pointed out that one atomic bomb on an arsenal would not be much different from the effect caused by any Air Corps strike of present dimensions. However, *Dr. Oppenheimer* stated that the visual effect of an atomic bombing would be tremendous. It would be accompanied by a brilliant luminescence which would rise to a height of 10,000 to 20,000 feet. The neutron effect of the explosion would be dangerous to life for a radius of at least two-thirds of a mile.

After much discussion concerning various types of targets and the effects to be produced, *the Secretary expressed the conclusion, on which there was general agreement, that we could not give the Japanese any warning; that we could not concentrate on a civilian area; but that we should seek to make a profound psychological impression on as many of the inhabitants as possible. At the suggestion of Dr. Conant the Secretary agreed that the most desirable target would be a vital war plant employing a large number of workers and closely surrounded by workers' houses.*

From the Franck Committee on a Noncombat Atomic Demonstration, 1945

Thus, from the "optimistic" point of view—looking forward to an international agreement on prevention of nuclear warfare—the military advantages and the saving of American lives, achieved by the sudden use of atomic bombs against Japan, may be outweighed by the ensuing loss of confidence and wave of horror and repulsion, sweeping over the rest of the world, and perhaps dividing even the public opinion at home.

From this point of view a demonstration of the new weapon may best be made before the eyes of representatives of all United Nations, on the desert or a barren island. The best possible atmosphere for the achievement of an international agreement could be achieved if America would be able to say to the world, "You see what weapon we had but did not use. We are ready to renounce its use in the future and to join other nations in working out adequate supervision of the use of this nuclear weapon."

1. What conclusion was reached by the Interim Committee on Military Use of the Atomic Bomb?

2. What conclusion was reached by the Franck Committee on a Noncombat Atomic Demonstration?

3. What goals were being considered in the discussion of why to use the bomb?

4. Compare the ways the effects of the atomic bomb are characterized in the two excerpts.

5. By synthesizing the two sources, what conclusions can you draw about the decision to use atomic bombs against Japan?

Critical Thinking Skills Activity 26 | Analyzing Information

When you research a topic, you have to analyze the information you find in order to understand why it was written, what is being said, and how it is significant.

DIRECTIONS: Read the following excerpt from British prime minister Winston Churchill's memoirs *Triumph and Tragedy.* Think about its historical context, the writer's motivation, the point of view it presents, and possible ways that it may be biased. Then answer the questions that follow on a separate sheet of paper.

The 1944 Percentage Deal

The moment was apt for business, so I said, "Let us settle about our affairs in the Balkans. Your armies are in Rumania and Bulgaria. We have interests, missions, and agents there. Don't let us get at cross-purposes in small ways. So far as Britain and Russia are concerned, how would it do for you to have ninety per cent predominance in Rumania, for us to have ninety per cent of the say in Greece, and go fifty-fifty about Yugoslavia?" While this was being translated I wrote out on a half-sheet of paper:

Rumania	
Russia	90%
The others	10%
Greece	
Great Britain	90%
(in accord with U. S. A.)	
Russia	10%
Yugoslavia	50–50%
Hungary	50–50%
Bulgaria	
Russia	75%
The others	25%

I pushed this across to Stalin, who had by then heard the translation. There was a slight pause. Then he took his blue pencil and made a large tick upon it, and passed it back to us. It was all settled in no more time then it takes to set down.

Of course we had long and anxiously considered our point, and were only dealing with immediate war-time arrangements. All larger questions were reserved on both sides for what we then hoped would be a peace table when the war was won.

After this there was a long silence. The penciled paper lay in the centre of the table. At length I said, "Might it not be thought rather cynical if it seemed we had disposed of these issues, so fateful to millions of people in such an offhand manner? Let us burn the paper." "No, you keep it," said Stalin.

—From *Triumph and Tragedy* by Winston Churchill

1. What was being decided at the meeting?

2. What does the word *offhand* mean and why was it used in the final paragraph?

3. Write a few sentences explaining the significance of this account in providing an understanding of the end of the war.

4. How might this account of the meeting differ from one that might appear in the newspaper?

CHAPTER 26

★ HISTORY AND GEOGRAPHY ACTIVITY 26

The Blockade of Japan

For ten weeks, Allied planes and submarines had trailed the Japanese supply convoy, eliminating its ships until only one was left, the *Sarawak Maru*. Finally, on March 20, 1945, that tanker, too, sank in a seething cloud of fire. How did the fate of the *Sarawak Maru* foreshadow the surrender of Japan?

The war between the Allies and Japan in the Pacific was fought over immense stretches of ocean that prevented rapid movement except by air. This meant that ships traveling the long sea-lanes were vulnerable to attack.

Japan, as a nation of islands with limited natural resources, depended heavily on shipping to bring in raw materials from its overseas conquests. It imported almost all of the oil needed to fuel its war machine, along with 80 percent of the iron ore it used to build ships. Half of its food also came from outside the home islands.

Recognizing this weakness, Allied strategists targeted Japan's merchant fleet. From the pitching decks of aircraft carriers, U.S. planes led the attack on the lifelines of the Japanese war machine. By 1944, the flow of resources was in such peril that the

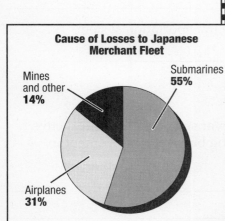

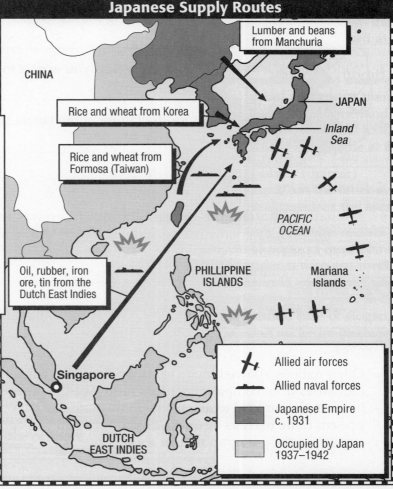

Raw materials streaming toward Japan were cut off by an Allied blockade. Not only did the Allies sink ships sailing between the resource-rich Dutch East Indies and Japan, but Allied planes also dropped mines into the waters of Japan's vital Inland Sea, sharply curtailing movement among the home islands themselves.

HISTORY AND GEOGRAPHY ACTIVITY 26 (continued)

Japanese took a desperate measure—kamikaze, or suicide, plane attacks on U.S. ships. A shortage of planes, however, undermined this strategy, and the relentless campaign against Japanese supply lines continued. Submarines, planes, and sea mines destroyed 90 percent of Japan's shipping by August 1945, and the depleted war machine faltered.

Barriers can have a dramatic effect on the movement of people, products, and ideas. Evaluating barriers to movement can disclose an opponent's weakness during war or reveal causes and effects to historians.

Barriers are not necessarily forbidding landforms such as mountain ranges. The Japanese had to bring oil 2,500 miles (4,000 km) from the Dutch East Indies to the home islands. For them, distance over open seas proved a barrier.

How readily movement takes place also depends on transportation. Japanese transportation failed when most of Japan's available ships were destroyed and it had little iron to build more.

APPLYING GEOGRAPHY TO HISTORY

DIRECTIONS: Answer the questions below in the space provided.

1. Why do we need to evaluate barriers to movement?

   _____

2. Which of Japan's wartime imports would you expect to be the last to be disrupted? Why?

   _____

3. What was the chief reason for the failure of the Japanese transportation system?

   _____

Critical Thinking

4. **Evaluating Information** Unlike Germany, Japan was never subjected to a destructive land invasion by enemy troops. Explain this by evaluating barriers to movement in Europe and in the Pacific.

   _____

   _____

Activity

5. Other nations allowed Japan to set up economic barriers to protect its struggling industries from competition after World War II. Some economists believe that trade barriers are harmful to all nations in the long term. From what you know about Japan's present trade barriers against U.S. products, do you agree with this theory? Explain your answer in one paragraph.

Time Line Activity 26

World War II

Background After World War I, territorial aggression and minor conflicts during the 1930s laid the groundwork for another major war. Tensions among European nations had become so strong by 1939 that it took only a spark—Germany's invasion of Poland—to ignite World War II.

DIRECTIONS: Read the time line. Then, for each outcome listed below, write the year and event that led to that outcome.

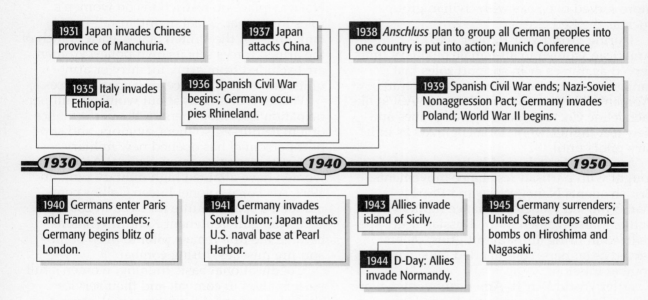

1931 Japan invades Chinese province of Manchuria.

1937 Japan attacks China.

1938 *Anschluss* plan to group all German peoples into one country is put into action; Munich Conference

1935 Italy invades Ethiopia.

1936 Spanish Civil War begins; Germany occupies Rhineland.

1939 Spanish Civil War ends; Nazi-Soviet Nonaggression Pact; Germany invades Poland; World War II begins.

1930   **1940**   **1950**

1940 Germans enter Paris and France surrenders; Germany begins blitz of London.

1941 Germany invades Soviet Union; Japan attacks U.S. naval base at Pearl Harbor.

1943 Allies invade island of Sicily.

1945 Germany surrenders; United States drops atomic bombs on Hiroshima and Nagasaki.

1944 D-Day: Allies invade Normandy.

1. Nation is divided; Germans occupy the capital and the northern half while collaborationist government is set up in southern part in the city of Vichy.

   Year _____   **Event** _____

2. Complete devastation of cities forces Japan to surrender.

   Year _____   **Event** _____

3. Germany and Italy aid the Nationalist forces led by Franco against the opposing Loyalist forces.

   Year _____   **Event** _____

4. Foreign aggression in the Pacific brings the United States into the war.

   Year _____   **Event** _____

5. Germany occupies and annexes Austria.

   Year _____   **Event** _____

6. Counterattack launched to roll back Axis forces from Italian peninsula.

   Year _____   **Event** _____

Linking Past and Present Activity 26

Women in Warfare

THEN "Is there any regulation which specifies that a Navy yeoman be a man?" That simple question solved a major problem—a shortage of sailors—for Secretary of the Navy Josephus Daniels during World War I. Allowed to enlist in the navy in 1917, American women served in non-combat roles ranging from clerks to electricians to nurses. About 33,000 women served in the United States Army, Navy, and Marine Corps during the war. Thousands more served overseas with civilian groups such as the Red Cross.

During World War II, over 100,000 American women in all-female auxiliary units served as nurses or in support roles that ranged from teaching to repairing aircraft. Women's Air Force Service Pilots (WASPs) like Jacqueline Cochran, who ferried planes and flew test flights, were not recognized as military pilots until 1977.

Yugoslav, French, and Italian women fought with partisan resistance movements. British agents Nancy Wake and Pearl Witherton led French resistance fighters into battle. Many women in the Russian army specialized in firing anti-aircraft guns; others served as snipers, commanded tanks, or flew combat missions.

After World War II, American women were allowed to join the regular military. However, women could make up no more than 2 percent of the armed forces and could not be promoted beyond a certain rank. Nearly 10,000 American women served in Vietnam, 8 of whom died. During the 1970s, the Armed Forces began training women as military pilots. Laws restricting women's participation in combat were repealed in the 1990s.

NOW Today, the roughly 200,000 women who serve in the military make up nearly 15 percent of America's armed forces. Women have served in military actions in Somalia, Haiti, Bosnia, and the Persian Gulf region, and they are eligible for most jobs in the United States military.

The extent of women's integration into the military, however, varies according to national policy. Belgium, Canada, Holland, and Norway place no restrictions on women's roles in combat. Israel maintains all-female tank units. In the United States, each branch of the armed forces sets its own policy. Women are excluded from army infantry or armor units, submarine service, and special forces.

While reservations about women's full participation in combat persist, the performance of female nurses, soldiers, aviators, and support personnel has opened new military opportunities for women. Several American women have attained high military rank. In 1999, Air Force colonel Eileen Collins commanded a space shuttle mission. In 2001, Navy top gun lieutenant Kendra Williams became the first female pilot to drop bombs and fire missiles during combat.

Coeducational basic training, women's full participation in combat, and their service aboard ships are still controversial issues. However, America recognized the value of women's military service in 1997 when the Women in Military Service for America Memorial was dedicated in Arlington National Cemetery. This site honors the 1.8 million women who have served in the American military since the Revolutionary War.

CRITICAL THINKING

Directions: Answer the following questions on a separate sheet of paper.

1. **Making comparisons:** Compare and contrast the military roles available to American women during World War I with those available today.

2. **Making inferences:** Why do you think American women have more military opportunities now than in World War II?

3. **Synthesizing information:** Speculate about the future of women in warfare. Do research in the library or on the Internet to learn about how things may change in the future for women serving in the military. Write a brief description of one change that could occur and explain why you think this change may or may not happen.

People in World History Activity 26

Profile 1

Joseph Stalin (1879–1953)

The guilt of Stalin and his immediate entourage . . . for the mass repressions and lawlessness they committed is enormous and unforgivable.

Mikhail Gorbachev in a 1987 speech on the
anniversary of the Russian Revolution

Joseph Stalin rose from a life of poverty to become the dictator of the Soviet Union from 1929 to 1953. A brutal ruler, he systematically imprisoned or killed anyone who opposed his decisions. As a result, he was feared and hated around the world. Nonetheless, Stalin helped transform the Soviet Union from an undeveloped country into an industrial and military giant.

When Stalin was 19 years old, he joined a secret group of Marxist revolutionaries. Social and economic conditions were very bad in Russia. Farmers were starving; factory workers could not earn enough to live. Czar Nicholas restricted education, forbade student groups, and censored newspapers.

Using various false names, Stalin helped organize strikes and set up a secret press. He was arrested and imprisoned many times during these years. In 1904 he joined the Bolsheviks, a wing of the Russian Marxist movement. By 1912, Stalin was one of their inner group of leaders.

World War I was very harsh time for Russia. Food shortages led to riots and strikes. On March 15, 1917, the czar was forced from his throne. Vladimir Ilyich Lenin took charge. In November 1917, the

Bolsheviks seized control of the government. During the civil war that followed, Stalin was appointed to the Politburo, the policy-making committee of the Russian Communist Party. From this position of power, he plotted to become dictator. When Lenin died in 1924, Stalin continued to maneuver into power, destroying his rivals along the way. Five years later, Stalin became dictator of the USSR, rejecting many of Lenin's policies.

In 1929, Stalin transferred control of all farms to the government. Farmers who resisted collectivization were exiled or killed—more than a million in all. In the 1930s Stalin purged millions more, anyone who opposed him. During World War II, he first allied Russia with Germany, but in 1943, when Hitler invaded the Soviet Union, Stalin joined forces with the Allies.

After the war, Stalin cut off all contact with non-Communist countries. Even after his death, many Communist countries ruled as he had done—a style of government known as Stalinism. Nikita Khrushchev, Stalin's successor, initiated a de-Stalinization program from 1956 to 1964 to reverse many of Stalin's policies.

CHAPTER 26

REVIEWING THE PROFILE

Directions: Answer the following questions on a separate sheet of paper.

1. Why did Stalin become a Marxist?

2. Why did Stalin join forces with the Allies during World War II?

3. **Critical Thinking** Evaluating Information. What words could you use to describe Stalin and his type of leadership?

People in World History Activity 26

Profile 2

CHAPTER 26

Anne Frank (1929–1945)

In spite of everything I still believe that people are really good at heart.

Anne Frank

Many people keep a diary and generally keep it to themselves. A few diaries, however, have a place in world history. One is the diary that in 1947 was published under the title *The Diary of a Young Girl*. More commonly known as Anne Frank's diary, it is one of the classics of war literature.

When World War II started, Annelies Marie Frank was a Jewish girl living in the Netherlands. The family had moved there from Germany because Anne's father, Otto, saw how bad life under Hitler was going to be. The Germans, however, conquered the Netherlands. Anne had to transfer from a public to a Jewish school. What Otto Frank feared would happen in Berlin was happening in Amsterdam.

Jews everywhere under Nazi rule were facing deportation. The Franks made a desperate decision. To try to escape the grip of the Nazis, in 1942, the family and four other Jews went into hiding in the back office and warehouse of Otto Frank's food business.

With the help of non-Jewish friends, the group hid successfully for over two years. During this time Anne wrote in her famous diary. Its style is grown up beyond Anne's years, and the diary shows Anne's lively intelligence and open, passionate heart. It records her emotional growth as she entered adolescence, and it shows honestly her hopes, fears, desires, and emotions, from dreams of romance to sarcastic remarks about people. Anne constantly makes keen observations about people and the world, and the book is filled with almost every aspect of being human. Most famously of all, even as Europe burned beyond the walls of her hiding place and she knew she would probably die if discovered, Anne maintained her belief that human nature was essentially good.

Acting on a tip from informers, the Gestapo found the Franks and the others in 1944. They were sent to the extermination camp Auschwitz. Anne's mother died there. Anne and her sister died in Bergen-Belsen of typhus, but Otto survived Auschwitz. Friends who searched their hiding place after the group was discovered found Anne's diary, which Otto had published. It has been translated into more than 50 languages and is among the most widely read books of the twentieth century.

REVIEWING THE PROFILE

Directions: Answer the following questions on a separate sheet of paper.

1. What idea that Anne Frank expresses in her diary has most impressed people?

2. What happened to the Franks after the Gestapo discovered them?

3. **Critical Thinking** Evaluating Information. Anne Frank maintained a belief that people were essentially good. Is Anne Frank's belief correct? Why or why not?

PRIMARY SOURCE READING 26

Rena's Promise: A Story of Sisters in Auschwitz

World War II erupted in 1939 when Hitler invaded Poland. In July 1941, Nazi leaders set into motion a plan to exterminate all the Jews in Europe—the Holocaust. During the next four years, the Nazis rounded up millions of Jews and sent them to concentration camps such as Auschwitz. The following interview describes the experience of one woman sent to the death camp at Auschwitz. She was there from the early days until the camp was liberated by the Allies.

Guided Reading *In this selection, read to learn how the Jews were sorted for slave labor or death when they arrived at Auschwitz.*

The brakes squeal with such finality that we know instinctively that our journey has ended. The doors are pushed open to a dull gray haze. We blink at the light stinging our eyes. The sign reads AUSCHWITZ.

"Get out of the car," the Germans order. We shift from blank stares to the business of collecting our belongings.

"Go quick!" Men in striped caps and uniforms prod us with sticks, whispering under their breath, "Move quickly. We don't want to hurt you." The SS aim their guns, forcing these poor prisoners to hit us so that we jump from the car. And we jump, half dead, with our luggage, if we have luggage.

It is four feet to the ground. My knees, cramped from being stationary for so long, feel as if they will snap as I land. I turn to help the woman with her baby. A stick taps my shoulder, "Go quick." I look for the eyes belonging to the voice, but there are only hollow black holes staring into my face.

"Get in line!" Orders are sharp, punctuated by whips against shining leather boots.

"Throw your suitcases over there," the SS shout.

I place mine upright, neatly, next to the growing pile, then turn to ask one of the SS guards, "How are we going to find our suitcases later?" I figure I am a human being, I have a right to ask.

"Get in line and shut up!" he yells in my face, pointing his gun at me. The hair on my skin bristles. He doesn't see that I am human.

There is an odor I cannot identify. It is not from human waste or people who have not

bathed in days, although those smells are also prevalent. It is the scent of fear permeating the air around me. It is everywhere, in the eyes of the men and women around me, in our clothing and our sweat.

The baby isn't alive anymore, but its mother does not notice the limpness of the form in her arms. Her desperate grasp on its corpse spooks me. There is too much happening. Everything is so hurried, so haphazard, that there is no way to make sense of the situation. I look through the crowd for some direction, for someone to tell me why we are here and what will befall us. I see him. He stands before us, superior and seraphic [angelic], taking control, directing us to go this way or that. He is so neat and refined in his gray uniform; he is gorgeous. I smile into his blue eyes, hoping he will see me for who I am.

"Do you want to give up the child?" he asks the woman with the dead baby.

"No." Her head shakes frantically.

"Go over there," he says.

How kind of him not to point out to her that her infant is dead, I think to myself. How kind of him to send her over to the group who is obviously weaker. The elderly and the very young are gathered apart from those of us who are stronger, able to work long, hard hours. I have no idea how many men, women, and children are on the platform, but each of us is told to go either to the left or the right. The direction has no meaning to us. I wonder which way the man in the gray will tell me to go.

Parents try to hug their children before they are taken away. "We have to go work." They try to comfort each other. "You are young enough not to have to come work with us. Grandmama will take care of you, . . ." they assure their flesh and blood. "Everything will be okay, you'll see. You'll be happier if you're not with Mommy and Daddy." Then Mommy and Daddy are separated.

I cannot bear the sound of children crying. This is madness. My mind begins to whirl. Struggling to focus on something, anything, to keep me from screaming, I stare at the man in gray. He is so stunning I am sure he must be considerate too. His orders are always obeyed. The SS around us defer to him quickly, answering, "Heil Hitler!"

His finger points. I answer by walking to the side of the other able-bodied young women. On the other end of the compound, we envy the group that will not have to work. They will go someplace warm, somewhere where they will be taken care of. It is natural to think this way—we are human beings, we assume we will all be treated humanely. I watch the proceedings with semi-fascination before lapsing into the fog where nothing needs to make sense. This is not daydreaming, this is electric shock.

Trucks come and load up the old, the sick, and the babies. There is nothing nice or caring about the way they rush them. These feeble souls are herded onto the flatbeds like so many sacks of potatoes piled on top of one another. My stomach somersaults. For one sick moment it occurs to me that maybe they're not going to be treated as well as I've been thinking, but I chase that thought away. They're in a hurry, I chide myself. There are so many of us; they have only momentarily forgotten to treat them gently.

Many of the girls next to me wave good-bye to those being taken away. I watch their stricken faces realizing that my prayer has been temporarily answered. There is no one for me to wave to, and for one brief moment I feel a tiny shred of gratitude. At least when I said good-bye to my family it was not in this place. The tears around me are too plentiful, the pain too raw, as mothers and daughters are driven apart. I shut my eyes but I cannot shut my ears.

"Good-bye, Papa!"

"Good-bye, Mama!"

INTERPRETING THE READING

Directions *Use information from the reading to answer the following questions. If necessary, use a separate sheet of paper.*

1. Why did Rena ask the Nazis about finding her suitcase later?

_____

2. How did Rena feel about the group that did not have to work?

_____

Critical Thinking

3. **Making Inferences** How can you infer that the people being loaded onto the truck were being sent to death?

_____

4. **Determining Cause and Effect** Why do you think Rena tells her story in the present rather than the past tense?

_____

World Art and Music Activity 26

Billie Holiday

". . . [W]ithout feeling, whatever you do amounts to nothing," Billie Holiday wrote in her 1956 autobiography, *Lady Sings the Blues.* Among the many great singers of her era—Lena Horne, Sarah Vaughan, Ella Fitzgerald—Holiday stands out for the emotion she always brought to her performances.

DIRECTIONS: Read the passage below about this African American jazz singer, then answer the questions in the space provided.

Eleanora Holiday was born in Baltimore, Maryland, on April 7, 1915. Her father, Clarence, served in World War I and afterward traveled as a guitarist with a band. Holiday saw little of him during her childhood. Her mother, Sadie, worked as a maid. When her mother traveled to Philadelphia and then to New York for work, Eleanora was left with relatives in Baltimore. Because she was a tomboy and a fighter, Eleanora's father called her "Bill"; she changed it to Billie and remained Billie thereafter. Her other nickname, "Lady Day," was a combination of the "day" from Holiday and the "Lady" from a lifelong reputation for dignity and pride.

Holiday had to struggle all her life against racism, poverty, and domestic violence. Her life changed dramatically when she landed her first singing job—$18 a week, guaranteed, at a nightclub in Harlem.

She was an immediate success with the audiences and began making friends and contacts among the jazz greats of the day, such as clarinetist Benny Goodman and agent Joe Glaser. These contacts led to her first recordings. During the 1920s and 1930s, jazz

"I can't stand to sing the same song the same way two nights in succession, let alone two years or ten years. If you can, then it ain't music, it's close-order drill or exercise or yodeling or something, not music."

—From *Lady Sings the Blues* by Billie Holiday

musicians would record "singles"–records with only one song per side. Holiday received between $35 and $75 for each of these recordings. Although the record companies earned thousands from the sales of these records, she never received any royalties. As was common with many jazz artists, Holiday never learned to read music. Because much of jazz performance is improvisation, the ability to read music was not essential. For Holiday, the music had to come from inside.

Holiday toured for two years as the vocalist with Count Basie's band. Bands at the time consisted of a bandleader, who often composed most of the material the band played, 4 to 16 musicians, and a vocalist. The instruments included trumpets, trombones, saxophones, clarinets, drums, and piano. The bandleaders played instruments as well—Benny Goodman the clarinet, Louis Armstrong the trumpet, Duke Ellington the piano. While the bandleaders and musicians were usually men, the vocalists were nearly always women.

Like all African Americans, Holiday suffered under the Jim Crow laws, which were abolished in 1954. She

(continued)

World Art and Music Activity 26

was the only African American performer in Artie Shaw's band, and the band encountered a lot of racism and bigotry from waiters, hotel clerks, and restaurant owners who did not want to accommodate her. "Sometimes it was a choice between me eating and the whole band starving," Holiday wrote. "I got tired of having a federal case over breakfast, lunch, and dinner." Her colleagues in the band always supported her and tried to ensure that she was treated with respect during their travels. However, they met with a great deal of resistance and prejudice.

After her success with Artie Shaw's band, Holiday returned to New York and began singing regularly at a new club called Café Society. At clubs in Harlem and in midtown, African Americans performed, but audiences were whites only; entertainers were sometimes asked to "use the back door." Café Society, by contrast, was fully integrated. It was in this club that Holiday met the poet Lewis Allen, whose poem "Strange Fruit" became the song that Holiday called her "personal protest." It became her anthem—her most requested number and one with which she moved audiences to tears all over the world. The text of the poem deals with lynching—the "strange fruit" is a metaphor for the many African Americans who

were hanged from trees by white vigilante mobs in the South during the 1800s and 1900s.

By 1945, Holiday had become addicted to drugs. She sought treatment at a sanatorium and was promised confidentiality, but someone betrayed this promise, and Holiday was followed everywhere she traveled by federal agents. She was arrested in 1947 and served one year in a federal prison. After her release, Holiday's career received a severe setback; because of her criminal record, she could no longer sing in any club that sold liquor. So she appeared in concert halls and Broadway theaters, where she was very successful.

In 1954, Holiday began an extended concert tour of Europe, where she was free to sing in clubs again, as well as at the London Palladium and at other great halls. Her return to America in 1956 marked another successful concert at Carnegie Hall, another arrest for drug possession, and the publication of her autobiography, *Lady Sings the Blues.* She died in 1959 at the age of 44.

Holiday's recordings, never out of print, have won her immortality. Listeners respond to her clear singing voice and the strength and passion of her performances. Her life story has also been put on screen in a film entitled *Lady Sings the Blues,* starring Diana Ross.

Reviewing the Selection

1. What are the characteristics of a jazz band of the Depression era?

_____

2. How was Holiday's career changed by her convictions for drug possession?

_____

Critical Thinking

3. Identifying Central Issues Why do you think Holiday chose "Strange Fruit" as her special number?

_____

_____

4. Determining Cause and Effect How do you think Holiday's career would have been different had she not been an African American?

_____

_____

Answer Key

CHARTING AND GRAPHING ACTIVITY 5

1919—Country: India; forces struggling for control: nationalistic groups in India against the British; important leader: Mahatma Gandhi

1921—Country: Iran; forces struggling for control: elements of the ruling Qajar dynasty against nationalistic forces in the military; important leader: Reza Shah Pahlavi

1922—Country: Turkey; forces struggling for control: forces desiring to form a democratic form of government against the Ottoman sultan; important leader: Colonel Mustafa Kemal

1928—Country: China; forces struggling for control: nationalist forces against the communists; important leader: Chiang Kai-shek

1930—Country: Argentina; forces struggling for control: government of President Irigoyen against the military; important leader: Hipólito Irigoyen

1930—Country: Brazil; forces struggling for control: ruling oligarchy against the military; important leader: Getúlio Vargas

1934—Country: Mexico; forces struggling for control: foreign business interests, the government, and peasants; important leader: Lázaro Cárdenas

ECONOMICS AND HISTORY ACTIVITY 5

1. A recession is an economic downturn that is marked by a decrease in consumer spending and an increase in unemployment.

2. A stockholder owns a part of the business.

3. Socialism answers the second question of economics by saying that it wants government to determine how goods are produced. Some socialists want all industries to be government controlled. Other socialists want the government to control only certain industries, with other industries owned privately.

4. A bull market is one in which the overall market trend is growth and stock prices increase.

5. Stock prices are a reflection of people's perceptions about a company. A company's stock prices can go up even when the company is not making profits if people believe the company is stable and a good investment. In addition, if more people are willing to buy the stock than sell it, the prices will continue to rise.

6. A market economy is one in which the consumer or market forces determine what will be produced. In a command economy the government decides what will be produced and this need not have any relationship to what is actually wanted or needed in the market.

7. Answers will vary.

WORLD LITERATURE READING 5

1. going to jail; when a woman gets married

2. Possible answer: to show that he has no identity to these people; he has not yet become a human being to them

3. As a father himself, he identifies with the peddler's deep affection for his child. He also regrets the distance between himself and his own daughter.

4. Possible answer: He suggests that raising children requires heavy responsibilities and, sometimes, great personal sacrifices.

VOCABULARY ACTIVITY 23

Across

1. armistice

5. communism

6. ultimatum

10. alliance system

11. soviets

13. total war

15. provisional

16. mandate

17. war of attrition

Answer Key

Down

2. militarism

3. planned economy

4. entente

7. reparations

8. conscription

9. trench

12. propaganda

14. mobilization

SKILLS REINFORCEMENT ACTIVITY 23

1. **a.** the Russian Empire
   b. no
   c. the Russian Empire

2. **a.** from the south and the east
   b. Denikin and Kolchak

3. Petrograd, Kiev

4. British, French, Canadians, Italians, Serbs

5. Odessa, Simferopol

6. Polish

7. British, French, Canadians, Americans

CRITICAL THINKING SKILLS ACTIVITY 23

Answers may vary. Possible answers:

Event 1: Germany and Austria-Hungary form alliance.

Event 2: France and Russia form alliance.

Event 3: Russia counts on French support in Russian defense of Serbia.

Event 4: Germany gives France ultimatum to remain neutral.

Event 5: France ignores ultimatum.

Event 6: Germany declares war on France.

HISTORY AND GEOGRAPHY ACTIVITY 23

1. Each group interacted with the environment in different ways and so perceived it differently. The fertile plains were important to the farmers because they were good for crops. The hills were important to soldiers because they gave commanding views.

2. Farming preserved the environment and encouraged its life-giving properties; warfare destroyed the environment.

3. Answers will vary. Students might say that modern warfare would cause even greater damage to the environment because of the use of nuclear, chemical, or biological weapons.

4. Answers will vary. Students might say that factory owners would be interested in harnessing the power of the river and building factories on the plains.

5. Encourage students to answer the questions by using appropriate reference materials.

MAPPING HISTORY ACTIVITY 23

1. Romania, Serbia, Montenegro, Albania, Greece

2. because Gallipoli lay at a strategic point—at an opening of a seaway leading directly to Constantinople, the capital of the Ottoman Empire

3. They could then join their territories and move to assert control over the entire Balkan Peninsula.

4. **a.** Arrows should point to Skopje from Sofia and Belgrade. An arrow should point from Sarajevo to Albania. An arrow should also point from southeastern Austria-Hungary to Bucharest. Another arrow should point from Constanz to Bucharest and northeastern Bulgaria.
   b. Students should shade Austria-Hungary.
   c. Arrows should point to Budapest, Sofia, and Constantinople from Salonika and other points in Greece.

Answer Key

HISTORICAL SIGNIFICANCE ACTIVITY 23

1.–3. Small groups' answers to questions and individual students' editorials will vary. Both should reflect students' understanding and thoughtful reflection on the consequences to world peace and national stability of large refugee populations.

COOPERATIVE LEARNING ACTIVITY 23

Students should complete the activity and answer the Group Process and Quick Check questions. Have students share their responses with their groups or with the class as a whole.

HISTORY SIMULATION ACTIVITY 23

Students should work collaboratively in groups toward achieving the learning objective of the History Simulation Activity.

TIME LINE ACTIVITY 23

Answers may vary. Possible answers:
Cooperation:
Event: France and Russia sign military alliance; Entente Cordiale between France and Great Britain. **Explanation:** Alliance brings countries together to support one another against aggressors.

Event: President Wilson asks Congress to declare war to help Allies. **Explanation:** United States assists the Allied Powers.

Event: Signing of Treaty of Versailles. **Explanation:** Big Four work together to bring about peace agreement.

Conflict:
Event: Balkan Wars. **Explanation:** fighting for control of Ottoman territory

Event: Assassination of Archduke Francis Ferdinand. **Explanation:** event that sparked the war

Event: Austria-Hungary declares war on Serbia. **Explanation:** beginning of war

Event: Germans invade Belgium. **Explanation:** beginning of conflict along the Western Front

Event: France and Germany fight the First Battle of the Marne. **Explanation:** major battle

Event: Allied defeat at Gallipoli. **Explanation:** Ottoman Empire fights back against Allies.

Event: President Wilson asks Congress to declare war to help Allies. **Explanation:** United States enters war to defeat the Central Powers.

Event: Germans sign armistice. **Explanation:** end of German war effort

Event: Signing of Treaty of Versailles. **Explanation:** Terms for Germany are harsh; Germany becomes resentful and angry.

Revolution:
Event: Assassination of Archduke Francis Ferdinand. **Explanation:** Assassins try to throw Austrians out of Bosnia.

Event: Coup d'état topples provisional government in Russia. **Explanation:** This was a backlash against the provisional government's decision to remain in World War I.

Event: Civil war in Russia. **Explanation:** Bolsheviks fight to stay in power.

Event: Russia's White armies admit defeat. **Explanation:** Communists complete their revolution.

Internationalism:
Event: Wilson presents Fourteen Points. **Explanation:** original plan for greater international stability; League of Nations idea introduced

Event: Signing of Treaty of Versailles. **Explanation:** Along with other peace treaties, right of self-determination given to new nations; war ended through international agreement.

LINKING PAST AND PRESENT ACTIVITY 23

1. During World War I, few people understood the combat potential of aircraft. At first, planes were primarily used for scouting, although General Billy Mitchell coordinated air and ground attacks. In modern warfare, planes are used for everything from search-and-rescue missions to bombing. Superior aviation technology can be a decisive advantage, as the United States demonstrated during the Gulf War.

Answer Key

2. Answers may vary. Students who agree may cite the successful use of air power in Baghdad, Bosnia, and Afghanistan. Those who disagree may point out the importance of ground troops or naval forces and the ability of guerrilla forces to wage successful campaigns in hostile terrain.

3. Student summaries should identify the person or event they chose and explain why their choice is important to the history of air warfare. Students might choose a war hero, an inventor, a military strategist, or a milestone in aviation history. Sample response: Baron Manfred von Richthofen (1892–1918) was the leading ace of World War I. Known as the Red Baron, he shot down 80 Allied planes. When Roy Brown of Canada downed the Baron's Fokker over enemy lines, the Allies gave the Baron a hero's funeral.

PEOPLE IN WORLD HISTORY ACTIVITY 23, PROFILE 1

1. His death was the initial spark that began World War I.

2. He was bitter because he assumed that the throne would go to his younger brother because of his poor health.

3. He was expected to marry someone of equal rank.

4. His family was denied the rights guaranteed by his status, including any claims his children might have had on the throne.

5. Answers will vary. Possible answers: He would not have had much influence on history because he did not have the power as long as his uncle was emperor, his children could not be heirs, and he was in poor health.

PEOPLE IN WORLD HISTORY ACTIVITY 23, PROFILE 2

1. She moved to Switzerland to avoid being imprisoned in Russia for her revolutionary activities.

2. The Russian Revolution of 1905 was a key event for Luxembourg because it radically changed her thinking. She now believed that the revolution would begin in Russia, not Germany.

3. As a Marxist, she believed that power should be in the hands of the people, not in the hands of a government. She believed mass strikes were the best way for this to be accomplished.

4. Possible answers: Yes, because she dedicated her whole life to helping people. No, because her theories that communism would create economic equality were not sound, as the fall of communism demonstrates.

PRIMARY SOURCE READING 23

1. Industrial workers were important to the Bolsheviks because they could use them as examples to illustrate to other Russians that workers supported better living and working conditions. This would increase membership in the Bolshevik party.

2. Lenin feared that the Central Committee was setting the Bolsheviks up to do them harm. He appeared to think that it favored the Mensheviks over his party. If he could get his associate Gusev to increase Bolshevik representation at the party Congress, they could prevent any adverse decisions against them.

3. Lenin's associate needed to leave because the czar's secret police were watching his activities. If he were caught, all of Lenin's and his own work for the party Congress would be exposed, and possibly the code names of their operatives. He was told to save the party's money to spur agitators to action or to help others escape the czars' police.

4. to make sure workers' grievances would be heard

Answer Key

RETEACHING ACTIVITY 23

1907: Triple Entente forms; two opposing sides now exist, ready to fight

June 1914: Archduke assassinated; Austria-Hungary declares war on Serbia, after which other nations mobilize

August–September 1914: German offensive

September 6–10, 1914: First Battle of the Marne; both sides realize there will be no easy victory

1914–1918: neither the Germans nor the French could dislodge each other from the trenches they had dug for shelter

1916: costly and inconclusive engagements, such as the Battle of Verdun

later in 1916: costly and inconclusive engagements; tank introduced by British

April 1917: United States enters war; raises morale of Allies; major new source of money and war goods; helps beat German offensive

March–September 1918: Allies stop Germans outside Paris, Allied forces make a steady advance toward Germany

November 11, 1918: Germans sign armistice; Germany surrenders to the Allies

August 30, 1914: Tannenberg

1915: Gallipoli campaign

mid-1915: A German-Austrian army defeats the Russian army in Galicia, nearly knocks Russia out of war

March 1918: Treaty of Brest-Litovsk

early-1919: Paris Peace Conference; representatives of 27 Allied nations meet in Paris to finalize peace treaties

June 28, 1919: Treaty of Versailles; Wilson gets League of Nations, Germany is heavily punished

ENRICHMENT ACTIVITY 23

1. to American women

2. It is trying to get women to buy government bonds to support the war effort.

3. The homey, maternal look of the woman is an emotional appeal to mothers to support their sons and husbands who have gone off to war.

4. The outstretched hands signify a request, or plea for assistance. Open arms also show giving and generosity.

5. to patriotism, pride, family devotion, heroism, generosity.

6. By placing the images in the background, the artist is hinting at the war as a type of reminder of the current situation. If these images were in the foreground, they may have distracted from the main idea and purpose of the poster.

7. Posters will vary, but should be judged on the directness of the messages and their persuasive effect.

WORLD ART AND MUSIC ACTIVITY 23

1. writing hit songs; writing hit Broadway musicals; inspiring American troops with "Over There" through two world wars

2. 8 to 20 short sketches including child performers, trained animal acts, circus acts, musical numbers, and comic scenes

3. Answers will vary. Possible answer: Cohan's patriotism is illustrated in the fact that his songs and shows are distinctly American in subject matter and in style. Such typical Cohan tunes as "I'm a Yankee Doodle Dandy" and "Give My Regards to Broadway" celebrate America. His shows paved the way for a distinctly American art form, the Broadway musical. Such patriotic songs as "Over There" were an important contribution to the war effort, as they built morale both among the soldiers and those left behind on the home front. Cohan also made a point of celebrating his birthday on July 4th.

4. Answers will vary. Possible answer: Cohan's shows proved that America did not have to depend on Europe for popular entertainment. In contrast to the shows popular at the time—the love stories of

Answer Key

European aristocrats—his shows were comic, patriotic, brassy spectacles with American settings and characters.

GUIDED READING ACTIVITY 23-1

1. They believed that if they could organize along national lines they could achieve peace.

2. the Triple Alliance (Germany, Austria-Hungary, Italy) and the Triple Entente (France, Britain, and Russia)

3. They were increasingly inclined to use violent strikes to achieve their goals.

4. If war did come, it would be highly destructive.

5. militarism, nationalism, and the desire to stifle internal dissent

6. the assassination of Archduke Francis Ferdinand and his wife Sophia

7. Russia employed full mobilization of its entire army.

8. The plan called for a two-front war with France and Russia.

9. through Belgium

10. Because Germany violated Belgian neutrality.

GUIDED READING ACTIVITY 23-2

1. avoided

2. propaganda

3. just

4. Paris

5. the First Battle of the Marne

6. stalemate

7. trench warfare

8. Verdun

9. planes

10. Germany

11. world conflict

12. colonies

13. submarine

14. battlefields

15. Authoritarian

16. positive

17. emancipation

GUIDED READING ACTIVITY 23-3

I. unprepared
   A. Czar Nicholas II
   B. women
   C. shooting
   D. Soviets
II. Marxist
   A. Lenin
      1. violent
      2. Land
   B. Winter Palace
   C. Council of People's Commissars
III. opposed
   A. material aid
   B. defeated
   C. murdered
IV. triumphed
   A. Red Army
   B. single-minded
   C. Red Terror

GUIDED READING ACTIVITY 23-4

1. offensives

2. psychological

3. Western Front

4. Social Democrats; democratic

5. communism

6. Rivalries

7. Paris

8. absolutism, militarism

9. Great Britain, pay

10. Treaty of Versailles

11. territory, disappeared

Answer Key

VOCABULARY ACTIVITY 24

1. Q
2. K
3. J
4. O
5. I
6. N
7. L
8. A
9. H
10. R
11. G
12. E
13. C
14. M
15. B
16. F
17. P
18. D

SKILLS REINFORCEMENT ACTIVITY 24

1. Bolshevism (early name for Soviet communism)
2. Fire represents something that is destructive and on the move.
3. houses, buildings, fields, etc., that represent a peaceful and ordered way of life
4. People in all countries of the world should be aware that Soviet communism is a danger to their traditional values.

CRITICAL THINKING SKILLS ACTIVITY 24

1. whether the United States should become part of the League of Nations
2. Senator B; 1.4 million Frenchmen died in the war and 4.3 million were wounded;

1.8 million Germans were killed; 8 million men died in all.
3. Possible answer: the use of factual data adds power to Senator B's speech
4. A stock market crash occurred in New York; the dollar was worth 4.2 million marks a decade earlier; Germany had printed new money to cover huge debts; this method of paying resulted in inflation.
5. Parliamentarian A argues that poor government planning is the cause of Germany's current economic problems; Parliamentarian B blames the Jews for these problems.
6. Parliamentarian A uses facts to support his or her argument; Parliamentarian B does not use any facts but appeals solely to the listener's emotions.

HISTORY AND GEOGRAPHY ACTIVITY 24

1. Tailors can find many customers in urban areas.
2. In the open areas of eastern Europe, the Jews were primarily agricultural.
3. Answers will vary. Students might say that community members work in local farms or mines and hike on local hills.
4. Answers will vary. Students might say that as people exert more control over their environment and as transportation improves, location's role diminishes.
5. Answers will vary. Possible answers: The city should be built in a central location that could serve as a transportation hub and encourage industry.
6. Answers will vary. Students living near rivers might suggest bottling the water and selling it to water-deprived areas; those living near plains might suggest growing plants that could be distilled into alternative fuels.

Answer Key

MAPPING HISTORY ACTIVITY 24

Students' keys and arrows should be appropriately color-coded.

1. One arrow should point from Greece to Turkey, and another arrow should point from Turkey to Greece.

2. Arrows should point from Romania to Turkey, from Bulgaria to Turkey, and from Yugoslavia to Turkey.

3. Arrows should point from northern Poland to Germany, from southern Poland to Germany, from western Czechoslovakia to Germany, and from northeast France to Germany.

4. Arrows should point from Germany to Belgium, to the Netherlands, to France, to Switzerland, and across the Atlantic.

5. Arrows should point to Hungary from Romania, from northern Yugoslavia, and from eastern Czechoslovakia.

HISTORICAL SIGNIFICANCE ACTIVITY 24

1. Prices rise.

2. A financial panic occurs when fear spreads among investors that their stocks will lose value. As they sell their shares, they bring down the value of the stock, thus triggering more fear among investors and more selling.

3. Answers may vary. Possible answer: With information, fewer people might become scared by changes in the stock market, and panicked selling could be prevented.

4. Today much trading is done by computer.

5. If stock prices fell beyond a certain point, millions of computers would automatically sell their stocks, causing a crash.

6. If the stock market average falls by 50 points in too short of a time frame, computerized trading is suspended until prices begin to rise.

COOPERATIVE LEARNING ACTIVITY 24

Students should complete the activity and answer the Group Process and Quick Check questions. Have students share their responses with their groups or with the class as a whole.

HISTORY SIMULATION ACTIVITY 24

Students should work collaboratively in groups toward achieving the learning objective of the History Simulation Activity.

TIME LINE ACTIVITY 24

1. 1920

2. 14 years

3. 1935

4. a. Italy
   b. Mussolini

5. a. stock market crash
   b. 1929

6. 1922

7. 1933

LINKING PAST AND PRESENT ACTIVITY 24

1. While the United Nations can take military action, much of its work is devoted to preventing conflict. The United Nations has tried to eliminate the causes of war by promoting disarmament, raising standards of living in developing countries, and protecting human rights. To prevent a conflict from escalating, the United Nations might apply economic sanctions, send peace keepers, or encourage diplomatic solutions.

2. The two international organizations were founded for a similar purpose: promoting world peace. Both could take military action to preserve world peace, unless powerful nations blocked action. The structure of the United Nations has three elements in common with the League of Nations: a Council, a General Assembly,

Answer Key

and a Secretariat. However, the United Nations has three additional elements: an International Court of Justice, an Economic and Social Council, and a Trusteeship Council. The United Nations also works for peace and human welfare on a scale much larger than that of its predecessor.

3. Student research will vary. Some essays might include mention of the debate in Congress over the payment of back dues to the United Nations and the recent changes that have taken place in the management of the United Nations, which have appeased some members of Congress.

PEOPLE IN WORLD HISTORY ACTIVITY 24, PROFILE 1

1. She was the first woman passenger on a transatlantic flight. She made many brave and daring flights that paved the way for future generations of women and pilots.

2. Her airplane vanished in the Pacific Ocean. No one knows the details of this disappearance.

3. Answers will vary. Possible answers: She represents the indomitable human spirit, the lust for adventure, the desire to take risks and blaze new paths. She faced all odds as a woman in a man's profession and did not compromise.

PEOPLE IN WORLD HISTORY ACTIVITY 24, PROFILE 2

1. Eleanor Roosevelt was most interested in unionism, aid to the poor, and civil rights, especially those of African Americans and women.

2. She got the news agencies to hire more women reporters by holding press conferences for women reporters only. Those organizations that had no women reporters were forced to hire one or more in order not to be scooped.

3. The Marian Anderson concert was held at the Lincoln Memorial because of Lincoln's role in ending slavery. The site reminded everyone that being for civil rights and equality was essentially American.

PRIMARY SOURCE READING 24

1. Its purpose was to show the Germans as "barbarians and Huns," to emphasize their cruelty to Belgian civilians, and to make the British and Americans angry and ready to fight. It was more effective because it prepared and motivated the British soldiers for war and battle. German propaganda was less effective because it made the enemy ridiculous, not threatening, and, consequently, German soldiers were unprepared for the enemy's courage and stamina and felt they had been misled ("swindled").

2. It should always be addressed to the masses because its effect is aimed at the emotions, not the intellect.

3. Effective propaganda should make only a few points (slogans) and repeat them over and over until everyone understands; it must have an emotional appeal to the masses and should reach people at the lowest intellectual level.

4. A "glimmer of light" on the other side admits doubts and confuses the masses.

5. Answers will vary. Students should provide examples to support their opinions. For instance, students who see similarities between propaganda and advertising or political campaigning may refer to Hitler's discussion of method (use of slogan, emotional appeal) and audience (masses, reaching as many people as possible).

RETEACHING ACTIVITY 24

United States:
Cultural: *Birth of a Nation.* **Economic:** 1929 stock market crash sets off worldwide depression; Roosevelt and the New Deal. **Political:** Works Progress Administration.

Answer Key

Great Britain:
Cultural: use of radios increases. **Economic:** John Maynard Keynes; no longer world's trade leader. **Political:** Conservatives replace Labour Party.

France:
Cultural: poet Paul Valéry. **Economic:** French New Deal. **Political:** Popular Front; Treaty of Locarno

Italy:
Cultural: *Quo Vadis*. **Economic:** industrial and agricultural workers strike; high unemployment. **Political:** rise of fascism and Mussolini.

Germany:
Cultural: art reflects state goals; Hannah Höch uses photomontage; Hermann Hesse; *Kraft durch Freude*. **Economic:** huge war debts; high unemployment. **Political:** creation of Weimar Republic; rise of Nazism and Hitler.

Soviet Union:
Cultural: art reflects state goals. **Economic:** Lenin and NEP; economy near ruin; drought causes famine; Stalin and Five-Year Plan. **Political:** government purges.

ENRICHMENT ACTIVITY 24

1. a wedding

2. Uncle Sam, who represents the United States

3. foreign entanglements

4. the potential for the League of Nations (printed on book) to involve the United States in foreign entanglements

5. the U.S. Senate

6. According to the Senate, the ceremony is unconstitutional.

7. 1918, at the time of the Paris Peace Conference

8. Answers may vary. Possible answer: The cartoonist seems to side with the Senate. The expression "foreign entanglements" has negative connotations, and while the bride looks very determined, the groom

looks very scared. The "Senate" is like a hero who arrives to defend the Constitution and to save Uncle Sam.

WORLD ART AND MUSIC ACTIVITY 24

1. Dadaists rebelled against Western culture because they believed it caused World War I. It was meant to assault traditional culture and unleash the creative mind.

2. Dadaist art often mixed elements of traditional art while adding the elements of chance and imagination.

3. Answers will vary; however, rap songs include the Dadaist elements of shocking or assaulting the public and bending traditional forms of music and performance; "happenings" or performance art contain the elements of improvisation (chance) and sometimes shocking the public.

4. Answers will vary but may include folk songs or protest songs during and after the Vietnam War, songs or artwork of racial equality movements, or even log-cabin architecture that rebels against modern urban architecture.

GUIDED READING ACTIVITY 24-1

1. It tried to fulfill nineteenth century dreams of nationalism by creating new boundaries and new states.

2. They refused to ratify or approve the Treaty of Versailles.

3. by operating and using the Ruhr Valley mines and factories

4. It granted an initial $200 million loan for German recovery and opened the door for American investment in Europe.

5. reduce their military forces to make war less probable

6. a series of downturns in the economies of individual nations in the second half of the 1920s, and an international financial crisis involving the U.S. stock market

Answer Key

7. Nearly one British worker in every four was unemployed.

8. no outstanding political leaders, serious economic problems, and unemployment

9. In a free economy, depressions should be left to resolve themselves without government interference.

10. He pursued a policy of active government intervention in the economy.

GUIDED READING ACTIVITY 24-2

1. democratic
2. dictatorial
3. totalitarian
4. conquer
5. collective
6. Fascism
7. Benito Mussolini
8. socialism
9. disorder
10. secret
11. political
12. Communists
13. industrialization
14. socialist
15. Joseph Stalin
16. authoritarian
17. Francisco Franco

GUIDED READING ACTIVITY 24-3

I. Vienna
   A. racism, anti-Semitism
   B. nationalist
   C. *My Struggle*
II. Reichstag, or parliament
   A. pride
   B. right-wing
   C. Enabling Act

III. Aryan
   A. Rome
      1. terror, repression
      2. rearmament
   B. Churches, schools
   C. bearers
IV. ideas, policies
   A. racial
      1. Nuremberg
      2. Stars of David
   B. *Kristallnacht*

GUIDED READING ACTIVITY 24-4

1. mass, Marconi's, wireless
2. Broadcasting
3. *Quo Vadis; Birth of a Nation*
4. Nazism
5. eight-hour
6. dadaists
7. Surrealism
8. folk
9. "Stream of consciousness"
10. "heroic age of physics"
11. uncertainty

VOCABULARY ACTIVITY 25

1. F
2. G
3. I
4. L
5. E
6. A
7. J
8. K
9. C
10. D
11. B

Answer Key

12. H

13. C

14. F

15. D

16. A

17. E

18. B

SKILLS REINFORCEMENT ACTIVITY 25

1.–3. A sample student spreadsheet is shown at the bottom of the page.

4. Import value minus export value; +B2 − C2 would calculate the balance of trade for Argentina in 1989.

5. 1989: Brazil; 1999: Argentina, Brazil, and Chile

6. Mexico. While Mexico's imports and exports have increased greatly, the country still has a very unfavorable balance of trade.

CRITICAL THINKING SKILLS ACTIVITY 25

1. that "chronic wrongdoing" would be met with U.S. intervention

2. The U.S. intervened with an invasion of marines.

3. Possible answer: It might lead to resentment.

4. that of a good neighbor who respects himself and others

5. Cárdenas nationalized Mexico's oil wells.

6. The most likely choice is b. An invasion would show lack of respect for Mexico, but doing nothing would show lack of respect for oneself.

HISTORY AND GEOGRAPHY ACTIVITY 25

1. The European colonists split up Iraq without any regard for ethnic regions.

2. conflicts among ethnicities; between ethnicities and national governments; among national governments

3. Answers will vary. Possible answers: A new map might resolve tribal conflict but encourage international conflict. Instead of forcing people to resolve their conflicts, the new borders might only encourage more conflict.

4. Answers will vary. Possible maps might show how forming a Palestinian state could resolve conflict in the Middle East or how forming a Masai state might resolve conflict in East Africa.

MAPPING HISTORY ACTIVITY 25

Students will not be able to show the exact route from the description provided, but they should indicate the general direction (west, then north, then northeast) of the march and the area covered.

	A	B	C	D	E	F	G
1	Country	1989 Import Value	1989 Export Value	1989 Balance of Trade	1999 Import Value	1999 Export Value	1999 Balance of Trade
2	Argentina	$1.40	$1.00	($0.40)	$2.60	$4.90	$2.30
3	Brazil	$2.70	$4.80	$2.10	$11.30	$13.20	$1.90
4	Chile	$1.30	$0.70	($0.60)	$2.90	$3.10	$0.20
5	Peru	$0.80	$0.60	($0.20)	$1.90	$1.70	($0.20)
6	Mexico	$27.20	$24.90	($2.30)	$109.70	$86.90	($22.80)

Answer Key

1. mostly mountainous

2. approximately 900 miles (1,450 kilometers)

3. The army was fighting as it retreated, and these changes in direction could have been caused by battles.

HISTORICAL SIGNIFICANCE ACTIVITY 25

Answers may vary. Possible answers:

1. From an early age, Americans are taught to respect the freedoms of others and the democratic system that governs the country. The protection of the rights of the individual forms one of the cornerstones of a collective national identity.

2. There are many ways that the United States is distinct from other countries. Categories like language, population, geographical territory, political ideologies, economic systems, and cultural practices can be used to show these distinctions.

3. Nationalism means different things to different American citizens. These differences can often lead to internal conflict with the country. For example, some Americans whose families have been in the United States for a long time may think of themselves as "true" Americans and view those with more recent immigrant backgrounds as outsiders. As enslaved or conquered peoples, African Americans and Native Americans may have a different conception of nationalism from those who have immigrated to the United States. Likewise, citizens who feel their opportunities are limited because of race, class, or gender discriminations will view the United States differently from those who do not experience such discriminations.

4. Since its founding, the United States has become a major global power. This change affects not only how American citizens view themselves, but also how other nations view the United States. Because people hold different ideas of what it means to be an American, the concept of nationalism is constantly changing and is frequently at the focus of political debates and protests.

COOPERATIVE LEARNING ACTIVITY 25

Students should complete the activity and answer the Group Process and Quick Check questions. Have students share their responses with their groups or with the class as a whole.

HISTORY SIMULATION ACTIVITY 25

Students should work collaboratively in groups toward achieving the learning objective of the History Simulation Activity.

TIME LINE ACTIVITY 25

Answers will vary.

Causes: Turkish government . . . , Balfour Declaration . . . , Gandhi protests . . . , Oil is discovered . . . ;

Results: Turkish Republic . . . , Chiang Kai-shek . . . , Japanese forces . . . , President Roosevelt . . . , Mao's troops . . . , Vargas establishes . . . .

LINKING PAST AND PRESENT ACTIVITY 25

1. Each of the world's major monotheistic religions venerates sacred sites in Jerusalem. In addition, Palestinians and Israelis claim Jerusalem as their political capital.

2. Jerusalem has great symbolic and political importance to both Muslims and Israelis. If their conflicting claims to the city could be worked out, both sides would have defined their political identities and protected sites important to their religious traditions, and the cycle of violence in the region might cease.

3. Answers will vary, depending on current events. Students' summaries should briefly report a recent development and explain its significance in the greater picture of Jerusalem. For example, in November 2001, Israeli archaeologists claimed that additions to the Al-Aqsa

mosque were damaging the remains of the first and second temples over which they had been built. Fundamentalist Muslims say no evidence of the temples has been found and claim that the site is sacred only to Islam. The disagreement is part of an ongoing dispute over Temple Mount that at times has turned violent. Each side accuses the other of seeking exclusive control of the sacred site.

PEOPLE IN WORLD HISTORY ACTIVITY 25, PROFILE 1

1. The movement to establish a Jewish national homeland was called Zionism after the hill in Jerusalem named *Zion*. It is believed King David established his capital there, and the word Zion occurs frequently in the Old Testament as a name for Jerusalem.

2. The crowning achievement of Chaim Weizmann's life was becoming the first president of the Jewish national homeland, Israel.

3. Yes, it does. The bias comes in referring to the countries of Europe and the United States as the "civilized nations of the world." Herzl implies here that other nations, for example China and Egypt, are not civilized. Accept a dissenting student answer if it is reasoned well.

PEOPLE IN WORLD HISTORY ACTIVITY 25, PROFILE 2

1. Supported by the Christian leaders, Haile Selassie toppled the new emperor in 1916. He became the regent and heir to the throne. In 1928, Haile Selassie took the title *Negus*. He was crowned emperor in 1930 when Empress Zauditu died.

2. Widespread unemployment, inflation, and starvation created great dissatisfaction with his leadership.

3. All nations are equal, none should think itself superior to another. Selassie was referring to Italy's invasion of Ethiopia. He was appealing to the League of Nations for help.

PRIMARY SOURCE READING 25

1. The two countries were partners in setting up oversight of the new mandates and competitors in preserving economic opportunities throughout the Arab states.

2. The tariffs would remain the same for a period of twenty years with no increase unless Britain and France agreed.

3. to foster peaceful relations among dominant nations of the world and to continue in their self-proclaimed role as protectors of the Arab state

RETEACHING ACTIVITY 25

I. A. Leads movement that overthrows the shah.
   B. Creates dynasty called Pahlavi.

II. A. Educated in Great Britain.
    B. Argues that British rule was destroying the traditional culture of the peoples of Africa.

III. A. Needs the expertise of the Soviet Union.
     B. Forms alliance with Communist Party.

IV. A. Good Neighbor policy keeps U.S. troops from entering Mexico.
    B. Establishes PEMEX to run the oil industry.

V. A. Vargus establishes a Fascist-like state in Brazil.
   B. Policies help Brazil become Latin America's chief industrial power.

ENRICHMENT ACTIVITY 25

1. Answers will vary. Possible summary: The tax on salt affects everyone, especially the poor and the weak, by forcing them to pay a high price on an essential

Answer Key

commodity that they could make them-selves.

2. It was an obviously unjust law that affected everyone and that was especially hard on the poor and the weak.

3. Despite conflicts among different religious groups, all could be involved in this campaign.

4. The government had stolen something that belonged to the people and made them pay heavily for it.

5. This tactic might have confused and embarrassed the British government, since they would not want to appear to contradict themselves.

6. By exposing the truth—that the government was charging high prices for something that should have been free or very cheap—Gandhi motivated many people to participate in the campaign, thus giving it great force.

WORLD ART AND MUSIC ACTIVITY 25

1. the National Preparatory School, Ministry of Education, and National Palace

2. the history and life of Mexico and Mexicans

3. because he believed that his artwork belonged to all the people

4. Answers will vary. Possible answers: On a literal level, the dead peon is being liberated from ropes and placed in a blanket. On a metaphorical level, the peon is being liberated from a life of toil on earth.

5. Answers will vary. Possible answers: He showed a people that had survived for thousands of years, sometimes under severe hardship. He showed many of their actual successes and the better future he envisioned for Mexicans. All this is uplifting.

GUIDED READING ACTIVITY 25-1

1. the Ottoman Empire

2. They supported Arab nationalist activities in the Arabian Peninsula.

3. genocide

4. Arabic elements were eliminated from the Turkish language, popular education was introduced, and all Turkish citizens were forced to adopt family names as in Europe.

5. Tehran

6. For the most part, Europeans created the Middle Eastern states.

7. the kingdom of Saudi Arabia

8. the Balfour Declaration

GUIDED READING ACTIVITY 25-2

1. British

2. independence

3. disappointment

4. Germany

5. ideals

6. practices

7. Kenya

8. high

9. reform

10. W.E.B. Du Bois

11. Marcus Garvey

12. Pan-Africanism

13. Senegal

14. self-rule

15. split

16. religious

17. Nehru

18. democratic

Answer Key

19. military

20. Communist

GUIDED READING ACTIVITY 25-3

I. Marxism
   A. imperialist
   B. Shanghai
   C. Nanjing
II. Mao Zedong
   A. peasants
   B. root
      1. surrounded
      2. Long March
      3. North China
III. constitutional
   A. dictatorial
      1. drained
      2. westernized
   B. "New Life Movement"
   C. censored

GUIDED READING ACTIVITY 25-4

1. foodstuffs, raw materials

2. investors; angered

3. militarily

4. Good Neighbor policy; rejecting

5. exports; 50 percent

6. revenue; industries

7. authoritarianism

8. oligarchy

9. dictator

10. peasants

11. Buenos Aires; São Paulo

VOCABULARY ACTIVITY 26

1. *Anschluss*

2. blitz

3. kamikaze

4. atomic bomb

5. amphibious

6. appeasement

7. demilitarize

8. Holocaust

9. Slavic

10. D-Day

11. blitzkrieg

12. sanctions

13. partisan

14. Czechoslovakia

SKILLS REINFORCEMENT ACTIVITY 26

1. The atomic bomb should be dropped without warning on a Japanese war plant to have a strong psychological effect on the population.

2. An atomic bomb should be first demonstrated in an international arena, rather than dropped on Japan, in order to prevent negative public opinion both at home and abroad.

3. saving American lives; ending the war; and achieving an international agreement to prevent future wars

4. The first excerpt, which supports military use of the bomb, emphasizes the visual and psychological effects of the bomb but downplays the human devastation. The second excerpt, which is against military use of the bomb, refers to the "horror" and "revulsion" that dropping the bomb would bring.

5. The two excerpts show that the question of using the atomic bomb for the first time was highly controversial and went through much debate. Some felt that immediate military objectives had to prevail, while others, sensing the public response such a bomb would produce, felt that it should come under international control and not be used for military purposes.

Answer Key

CRITICAL THINKING SKILLS ACTIVITY 26

1. They were deciding who would have control over the territories that the Allies had freed from Axis control and to what degree they would be able to influence the immediate postwar arrangements.

2. *Offhand* means "without forethought" and describes the way that the agreement appeared to have been reached. A single check mark signified Stalin's acceptance. Thus, seemingly without any discussion and without any input from the people concerned, the lives of millions living in Balkan Europe were decided.

3. Answers will vary. Possible answer: It is significant because it gives a firsthand account of a high-level meeting between Churchill and Stalin in which they decided who would get to control the territories they had reconquered. The excerpt describes how these two leaders reached an agreement that would affect the whole world. According to Churchill's account, these weighty matters were settled quickly with no debate or input from countries listed on the agreement.

4. The account given to newspaper reporters would not have the first-person point of view that Churchill had as a participant, nor would it likely reveal the brevity with which the decision had been made.

HISTORY AND GEOGRAPHY ACTIVITY 26

1. Evaluating barriers to movement can disclose an enemy's weakness during war or reveal causes and effects to historians.

2. Answers may suggest that imports from Korea would be the last to be interrupted, because the distance between Japan and Korea is less than the distance between Japan and its other sources of key materials.

3. The chief cause for the failure of Japanese shipping was destruction by submarines.

4. Answers should mention that Europe, being a continuous landmass, had no internal sea barriers to invasion after armies had landed on its shores in France and Italy. Allied armies could sweep into the heart of Germany in a relatively short time, especially since the distances involved were much smaller than the distances between Japan and nearby Allied bases. It is clear that the reason Japan was not subject to a destructive land invasion was that it was surrounded by ocean barriers. Thus barriers to movement both helped and hurt Japan's war effort.

5. Students may mention that nations that protect their economies with artificial tariffs and quotas inevitably invite retaliation from other nations. The result is that countries waste their own resources because of the artificial prices that result. Japan has a history of protecting its steel, automobile, and construction industries, as well as its agriculture.

MAPPING HISTORY ACTIVITY 26

1. the Soviet Union

2. Arrows should point from New York to locations in Europe, from Virginia to India, from Seattle to Aleutian Islands, from San Francisco to several locations in the Pacific, and from Los Angeles to India.

HISTORICAL SIGNIFICANCE ACTIVITY 26

1. In the 1930s, Germans attacked Jews, and the Nazi government took away their rights. During the war, Jews, Slavs, and Gypsies were imprisoned and killed in concentration and death camps.

2. The economy was strained by the need to bring the eastern part of Germany up to western levels of production; unemployment was high.

3. The economy in prewar Germany was also weak. In the 1920s, Germany suffered

Answer Key

from skyrocketing inflation, and the 1930s brought the Great Depression.

4. They were meant to prevent Nazi-like groups from forming and gaining power.

COOPERATIVE LEARNING ACTIVITY 26

Students should complete the activity and answer the Group Process and Quick Check questions. Have students share their responses with their groups or with the class as a whole.

HISTORY SIMULATION ACTIVITY 26

Students should work collaboratively in groups toward achieving the learning objective of the History Simulation Activity.

TIME LINE ACTIVITY 26

1. 1940; Germans enter Paris and France surrenders.

2. 1945; United States drops atomic bombs on Hiroshima and Nagasaki.

3. 1936; Spanish Civil War begins.

4. 1941; Japan attacks U.S. naval base at Pearl Harbor.

5. 1938; *Anschluss* plan to group all German peoples into one country is put into action.

6. 1943; Allies invade island of Sicily.

LINKING PAST AND PRESENT ACTIVITY 26

1. During World War I, American women were restricted to non-combat roles such as nursing and operations support. They were allowed to serve only because of the shortage of men. Today, women are part of the regular military. Most positions are open to women, except special forces, submarine service, and army infantry or armor units.

2. Answers will vary. Students might note that women have proved their ability to perform in the military, that gender discrimination is no longer legal, or that

warfare today relies less on strength and more on technical knowledge.

3. Student answers should identify a change that could occur and explain why they think this change is likely or unlikely to happen. Possible changes might include eligibility for full participation in combat, new standards for physical training, elimination of the "glass ceiling," full gender integration of the armed services, elimination of the double standard for misconduct, reduction in sexual harassment, changes in American attitudes towards women in the military, or new "firsts" achieved by female military personnel.

PEOPLE IN WORLD HISTORY ACTIVITY 26, PROFILE 1

1. Possible answer: Social conditions were very bad in Russia, and he believed that a total reorganization of the government through Marxism was the answer.

2. He needed the protection against Hitler's planned invasion of Russia.

3. Answers will vary. Possible answers: vicious, brutal, merciless, effective

PEOPLE IN WORLD HISTORY ACTIVITY 26, PROFILE 2

1. The idea from the diary that has most impressed people is the idea that people are essentially good.

2. Anne, her sister, and mother died in the death camps. Her father survived the camps.

3. Student answers will vary. Accept any answer that is relevant and thoughtful.

PRIMARY SOURCE READING 26

1. She felt that as a human being she had a right to know and to be treated with consideration.

Answer Key

2. She envied the group that would not have to work, thinking that they would go somewhere where they would be taken care of.

3. Answers will vary. Possible answers: by the brutal way the people were being treated, by Rena's "one sick moment" when she thought that the people were not going to be treated as well as she had been thinking

4. It makes the story more immediate and emotional; by creating empathy in the reader for the narrator, it makes readers understand that what happened in the past must never be forgotten or allowed to happen in the present.

RETEACHING ACTIVITY 26

United States: c,d,h,v,y
Great Britain: i,p,x
France: e,q,w
Soviet Union: g,r,u,z
Germany: a,j,l,s
Italy: f,k,m
Japan: b,n,o,t

ENRICHMENT ACTIVITY 26

1. almost twice as costly

2. **a.** Soviet Union
  b. about 7.5 million
  c. 37.5%

3. **a.** about 2.85 million
  b. greater

4. World War II

5. **a.** about 1.36 million
  b. 210,000
  c. because France surrendered to Germany early in the war and thus did not continue to fight them as they did throughout World War I

6. 29.5%

WORLD ART AND MUSIC ACTIVITY 26

1. male bandleader, 4 to 16 male musicians, female vocalist; bandleader was often a composer as well; instruments included trumpets, trombones, saxophones, drums, piano, clarinets; much of the music improvised, not written out

2. She could not legally sing in nightclubs, which sold liquor, because of her criminal record. Therefore she was limited to appearances in concert halls and theaters. It is possible that these limitations were a motive for her European tour, since this law did not apply outside the United States.

3. Possible answers: Holiday felt strongly about segregation and wanted to change Jim Crow laws and to eliminate racial prejudice. She felt that music was the best medium in which to protest, since she was heard by many thousands of people during her career and was always popular with the public despite the difficulties in her life offstage.

4. Answers will vary. Possible answers: Had Holiday been white, she would not have been subjected to the Jim Crow laws which prevented her from traveling in comfort, dining in restaurants, or getting hotel rooms in many places. The physical exhaustion caused by these difficulties may have prevented her from singing her best and the stress of these encounters may have contributed to her substance abuse.

GUIDED READING ACTIVITY 26-1

1. to the east, in the Soviet Union

2. the Third Reich

3. the Treaty of Versailles

4. The dissatisfied powers would be content and stability and peace would be achieved in Europe.

Answer Key

5. He boasted that the agreement meant "peace for our time" that Hitler would make no more demands.

6. that he would be known as the greatest German of them all

7. On September 1, 1939, German forces invaded Poland.

8. Manchuria had natural resources, which Japan needed.

9. Japan hoped the two countries would jointly attack the Soviet Union.

10. Japan decided to launch a surprise attack on U.S. and European colonies in Southeast Asia.

GUIDED READING ACTIVITY 26-2

1. speed

2. efficiency

3. blitzkrieg

4. surrendered

5. Britain

6. air and naval bases

7. harbors

8. communication centers

9. war industries

10. Soviet Union

11. winter

12. resistance

13. Pearl Harbor

14. Nationalist China

15. Hitler

16. unconditionally

17. against

18. Normandy

19. suicide

20. atomic

21. Hiroshima

22. Nagasaki

GUIDED READING ACTIVITY 26-3

I. English Channel; Moscow
  A. Heinrich Himmler; Germans
  B. forced
II. genocide
  A. Reinhard Heydrich
  B. extermination
  C. million
  D. Holocaust
  E. bombing
    1. countryside
    2. Hiroshima
III. "Asia for the Asiatics"
  A. resources
  B. Tokyo
  C. Burma-Thailand

GUIDED READING ACTIVITY 26-4

1. total

2. arsenal

3. African Americans

4. Japanese Americans

5. consumer goods; armaments

6. kamikaze; suicide

7. civilian

8. partition

9. Stalin

10. "an iron curtain"

ACKNOWLEDGMENTS

TEXT

11 "The Kabuliwallah" by Rabindranath Tagore. Copyright © 1916 by Macmillan, renewed 1944 by Rabindranath Tagore and Henry L.S. Polak.

24 From "Balm for Bosnia" by H.D.S. Greenway from the *Boston Globe,* copyright © 1996 by the *Boston Globe.*

33 Excerpts from *The Letters of Lenin,* translated and edited by Elizabeth Hill and Doris Mudie, Copyright © 1937 by Harcourt Brace & Company, reprinted by permission of the publisher.

61 Excerpts from *Mein Kampf* by Adolf Hitler, translated by Ralph Manheim. Copyright © 1943, renewed 1971 by Houghton Mifflin Company. Reprinted by permission of Houghton Mifflin Company. All rights reserved.

89 "The Sykes-Picot: 1916. Copyright © 1996–2001 The Avalon Project at the Yale Law School. Reprinted by permission.

103 From "The Interim Committee on Military Use of the Atomic Bomb, 1945" and "The Franck Committee on a Noncombat Atomic Demonstration, 1945" from *Major Problems in American Foreign Policy* edited by Thomas G. Paterson, copyright © 1989 by D. C. Heath and Company.

104 From *Triumph and Tragedy* by Winston S. Churchill. Copyright © 1953 by Houghton Mifflin Company. Copyright © renewed 1981 by the Honourable Lady Sarah Audley and the Honourable Lady Soames. Reprinted by permission of Houghton Mifflin Company.

117 From *Rena's Promise* by Rena Kornreich Gelissen with Heather Dune Macadam. Copyright © 1995 by Rena Kornreich Gelissen and Heather Dune Macadam. Reprinted by permission of Beacon Press, Boston.

121 From *Lady Sings the Blues* by Billie Holiday with William Duffy, copyright © 1956 by Eleonora Fagan and William F. Duffy.

PHOTOGRAPHS

21 Bettmann Archive

31 Bettmann Archive

32 Archive Photos

37 UPI/Corbis-Bettmann

47 *The Red Peril,* by Nelson Harding, copyright © 1919, *The Brooklyn Eagle.*

49 Alter Kaazyne Yivo Institute for Jewish Research

59 UPI/Corbis-Bettmann

60 Leo Rosenthal/PIX Inc.

65 GNAC/NMAM Dist. Reunion des Musees

87 Bernard Hoffman

88 AP/Wide World Photos

93 Philadelphia Museum of Art: Gift of Mr. and Mrs. Herbert Cameron Morris

115 UPI/Bettmann

116 Anne Frank Fonds/Archive Photos

121 Frank Driggs Collection/Hulton Archive/Getty Images

Teacher Notes

Teacher Notes

Teacher Notes